Memories
Reader's Corner

IMAGINATION
An Odyssey Through Language

Memories
Reader's Corner

Gail Heald-Taylor
General Consultant, Language Arts

 HARCOURT BRACE JOVANOVICH, PUBLISHERS

Orlando   San Diego   Chicago   Dallas

Printed in the United States of America

ISBN 0-15-332811-8

Acknowledgments

For permission to reprint copyrighted material, grateful acknowledgment is made to the following sources:

Curtis Brown, Ltd. and Scholastic Inc.: Adapted from *Sound of Sunshine, Sound of Rain* by Florence Parry Heide, illustrated by Kenneth Longtemps. Text copyright © 1970 by Florence Parry Heide; illustrations copyright © by Kenneth Longtemps.

Dial Books for Young Readers: Adapted from "I Never Asked for No Allergy" (Retitled: "An Allergy Is a Bothersome Thing") in *Philip Hall likes me. I reckon maybe.* by Bette Green. Copyright © 1974 by Bette Greene. From *Benjy in Business* (Retitled: "It Pays to Advertise") by Jean Van Leeuwen. Copyright © 1983 by Jean Van Leeuwen.

Dodd, Mead & Company, Inc.: Adapted from *An Eskimo Birthday* by Tom D. Robinson. Text copyright © 1975 by Tom Robinson.

Doubleday Publishing, a division of Bantam, Double-day, Dell Publishing Group, Inc.: Illustrations from *The Erie Canal* by Peter Spier. Copyright © 1970 by Peter Spier.

E. P. Dutton, a division of NAL Penguin Inc.: "The Case of the Missing Roller Skates" from *Encyclopedia Brown, Boy Detective* by Donald J. Sobol. Copyright © 1963 by Donald J. Sobol.

Farrar, Straus & Giroux, Inc.: "frog" from *Small Poems* by Valerie Worth. Copyright © 1972 by Valerie Worth.

Harcourt Brace Jovanovich, Inc.: From pp. 128-138 in "The Ghost in the Attic" from *The Moffats* by Eleanor Estes. Copyright 1941, 1969 by Eleanor Estes. "Arithmetic" from *The Complete Poems of Carl Sandburg* by Carl Sandburg. Copyright 1950 by Carl Sandburg, renewed 1978 by Margaret Sandburg, Helga Sandburg Crile, and Janet Sandburg.

Harper & Row, Publishers, Inc.: "What Night Would It Be?" from *You Read to Me, I'll Read to You* by John Ciardi. Copyright © 1962 by John Ciardi. Adapted text from pp. 7, 28, 38, 39, 49, 60, 61, and 62 in *Kickle Snifters and Other Fearsome Critters* by Alvin Schwartz. Text copyright © 1976 by Alvin Schwartz. Both published by J. B. Lippincott Co. From pp. 16-23, illustrations from pp. 20-21, and a portion of the

jacket from *Charlotte's Web*, written by E. B. White, illustrated by Garth Williams. Copyright 1952, 1980 by E. B. White; illustrations copyright renewed 1980 by Garth Williams.

Houghton Mifflin Company: "Paddington Goes to the Hospital" from *Paddington on Stage* by Michael Bond and Alfred Bradley. Copyright © 1974 by Alfred Bradley and Michael Bond.

Kaisei-Sha: Adapted from *The Crane Maiden* by Miyoko Matsutani. Text copyright © 1966 by Miyoko Matsutani. Originally published by Kaisei-Sha, Tokyo.

Alfred A. Knopf, Inc.: "Dreams" from *The Dream Keeper and Other Poems* by Langston Hughes. Copyright 1932 by Alfred A. Knopf, Inc., renewed 1960 by Langston Hughes.

Macmillan Publishing Company: "Some People" from *Poems* by Rachel Field. Published by Macmillan, New York, 1957. Adapted from pp. 37-45 and map of Underground Railroad in *Steal Away Home* by Jane Kristof, map by W. T. Mars. Text copyright © 1969 by Jane Kristof; illustration copyright © 1969 by W. T. Mars.

William Morrow & Company, Inc.: From pp. 142-161 in *Ramona the Brave* (Retitled: "Spunky Ramona") by Beverly Cleary. Copyright © 1975 by Beverly Cleary.

Parents Magazine Press: Adapted from *Mexicali Soup* by Kathryn Hitte and William D. Hayes. Text copyright © 1970 by Kathryn Hitte and William D. Hayes.

Prentice-Hall, Inc., Englewood Cliffs, NJ: Adapted from "The Monkey and the Crocodile" in *Jataka Tales*, retold by Ellen C. Babbitt. © 1912, renewed 1940.

G. P. Putnam's Sons: The Legend of the Bluebonnet, written and illustrated by Tomie dePaola. Text and illustrations copyright © 1983 by Tomie dePaola.

Random House, Inc.: "The Lion and the Mouse" from *Aesop's Fables*, retold by Anne Terry White. Copyright © 1964 by Anne Terry White.

Marian Reiner, on behalf of Eve Merriam: "Metaphor" from *It Doesn't Always Have to Rhyme* by Eve Merriam. Copyright © 1964 by Eve Merriam. All rights reserved.

Louise H. Sclove: "What the Gray Cat Sings" from *I Sing the Pioneer* by Arthur Guiterman. Copyright 1926 by

E. P. Dutton and Co., Inc., renewed copyright 1954 by Mrs. Vida Lindo Guiterman.

Simon & Schuster, Inc.: From *C D B!* by William Steig. Copyright © 1968 by William Steig.

Viking Penguin Inc.: From *The Midnight Fox* (Retitled: "The Black Fox") by Betsy Byars. Copyright © 1968 by Betsy Byars. From *Half a Kingdom* by Ann McGovern. Text copyright © 1977 by Ann McGovern. "Buying a Puppy" from *Merlin & The Snake's Egg* by Leslie Norris. Copyright © 1977, 1978 by Leslie Norris.

Jerry Vogel Music Company, Inc.: Text and melody line from "The Erie Canal" also known as "Low Bridge, Everybody Down" or "Fifteen Years on the Erie Canal." Copyright 1912, renewed 1940. Copyright assigned to Jerry Vogel Music Co., Inc., 58 West 45th Street, New York, NY 10036. Reproduction prohibited.

Beth P. Wilson: From *The Great Minu* by Beth P. Wilson. Text copyright © 1974 by Beth P. Wilson. This story is based on "The Honourable Minu," originally published in West African Folk Tales by George Harrap & Company Ltd., London, England.

Art Acknowledgments

Chuck Bowden: 248, 274, 406 (adapted from photographs from the following sources: 248, courtesy William Morrow and Company, Inc.; 274, courtesy Houghton Mifflin Company; 406, courtesy UPI); Susan David: 44, 131, 216, 330; Pat & Robin DeWitt: 20, 102, 188, 308, 400; Kitty Diamantis: 52, 166, 232, 374; George Ford: 88, 178, 250, 382; Sharon Harker: 276, 278, 279; Tony Kenyon: 277, 278; Christa Kieffer: 408; Ed Taber: 132–135; John S. Walter: 48.

Cover: Tom Vroman

Maps: Joanna Adamska Koperska

Unit Openers: Mila Lazeravich

Production and Layout: Helena Frost Assoc., Ltd.

Photo Acknowledgments

Bruce Coleman, Inc., © Tom Brakefield: 47; David de Vries: 46; Giorgio Gualco/U.P.: 46; © Dr. George Gerster: 50.

Contents

4 What a Character! 203

ix

1 Problems and Puzzles

TALKING ABOUT THE THEME

Look at the picture on page 1 and read the title.

1. What is happening in the picture?

2. How is a maze like a puzzle?

3. Why might people enjoy things like mazes and puzzles?

4. What types of puzzles or problems do you enjoy most?

5. How would you expect the selections in this unit to be alike?

Other Books About Problems and Puzzles

Bet You Can't! Science Impossibilities to Fool You by Vicki Cobb and Kathy Darling. Avon, 1983. These tricks may seem impossible, but they are not. They are easy as pie—if you know the secrets.

The Return of the Great Brain by John D. Fitzgerald. Dial Books, 1974. Young Tom can solve mysteries that puzzle everyone else. He gets himself into the middle of the problems he solves.

The Clever Princess by Ann Tompert. Lollipop Power, 1977. No one can solve the problems posed by the king's advisors. Princess Lorna comes along to save the day.

Focusing on "Arithmetic," "Pudden Tame," "Where R U?"

▶ Talk about what makes you smile and laugh. Ask questions about what your classmates say.

▶ Read the title of each selection. Think about what makes you smile and laugh.

- Which selections might be silly?
- What would you expect to read about in a poem about arithmetic?

▶ Enjoy the puzzles and poems you are about to read. Think about how the writers used the language to make their readers laugh. Think about what you would add to this chart.

Funny Words and Ideas	
"Arithmetic"	
"Pudden Tame"	
"Where R U?"	

Now turn the page and read the three selections. Then you will talk about silly things.

Arithmetic

A poem by Carl Sandburg

Arithmetic is where numbers fly like pigeons in
and out of your head.

Arithmetic tells you how many you lose or win if
you know how many you had before you lost or
won.

Arithmetic is seven eleven all good children go to
heaven—or five six bundle of sticks.

Arithmetic is numbers you squeeze from your head
to your hand to your pencil to your paper till
you get the answer.

Arithmetic is where the answer is right and
everything is nice and you can look out of
the window and see the blue sky—or the answer
is wrong and you have to start all over and
try again and see how it comes out this time.

4

If you take a number and double it and double it again and then double it a few more times, the number gets bigger and bigger and goes higher and higher and only arithmetic can tell you what the number is when you decide to quit doubling.

Arithmetic is where you have to multiply—and you carry the multiplication table in your head and hope you won't lose it.

If you have two animal crackers, one good and one bad, and you eat one and a striped zebra with streaks all over him eats the other, how many animal crackers will you have if somebody offers you five six seven and you say No no no and you say Nay nay nay and you say Nix nix nix?

If you ask your mother for one fried egg for breakfast and she gives you two fried eggs and you eat both of them, who is better in arithmetic you or your mother?

Illustrated by Sharon Harker

5

Pudden Tame

A folk rhyme

What's your name?
    Pudden Tame.
What's your other?
    Bread and Butter.
Where do you live?
    In a sieve.
What's your number?
    Cucumber.

Where R U?

Letter puzzles written
and illustrated by William Steig

I M N D L-F-8-R.

(I am in the elevator.)

D D-R S N D I-V.

(The deer is in the ivy.)

D C-L S N D C.

(The seal is in the sea.)

Think about the selections. Finish the chart on page 3. Then answer the questions.

Think and Discuss

1. Use your chart. What word picture does the writer use in the first line of "Arithmetic"? Why does the writer use that word picture?

2. What word rhymes with *number* in "Pudden Tame"? Why does the writer choose that rhyming word?

3. Use your chart. What is the main joke that the writer uses in "Where R U?" How do you solve the puzzles in this selection?

4. How do the pictures the writer has drawn for "Where R U?" add to the humor of the piece?

5. Do the rhyming answers in "Pudden Tame" make sense? What other silly response to "What's your name?" would you use?

6. Why do these selections all belong to a unit about challenges and problems?

WORK IN A GROUP

Which of the three selections is funniest? Why? Ask questions about what your classmates say. Share your answers with the class.

Focusing on "The Case of the Missing Roller Skates"

▶ Talk about what makes someone an honest person. Ask questions about what your classmates say.

▶ Read the title of the story. Think about what you know about honest people.

- What kind of story do you think this will be? Tell why you think as you do.
- What problem would you guess the main character faces? What might have caused it?

▶ As you read this story, think about the steps Encyclopedia Brown follows to solve his problem. Think about what you would add to this chart.

Encyclopedia's Problem

Steps to Solving Problem

1.

2.

3.

Solution

Now turn the page and read "The Case of the Missing Roller Skates." Then you will talk about honesty.

The Case of the Missing Roller Skates

A story by Donald J. Sobol
Illustrated by Bert Dodson

Mr. Brown may be the Chief of Police of Idaville, but it is his son Leroy who puts the clues together and provides the solutions to many police cases. His success in solving his father's cases leads Leroy, also known as Encyclopedia Brown, to form his own detective agency with Sally Kimball as his partner. Then one day Encyclopedia finds that he himself is the victim of a crime.

Between nine and nine-thirty on Tuesday morning Sally Kimball's roller skates disappeared from the waiting room in Dr. Vivian Wilson's office.

And where was Encyclopedia Brown, boy detective? He was not ten feet away from the scene of the crime. He was sitting in a chair, with his eyes shut and his mouth wide open!

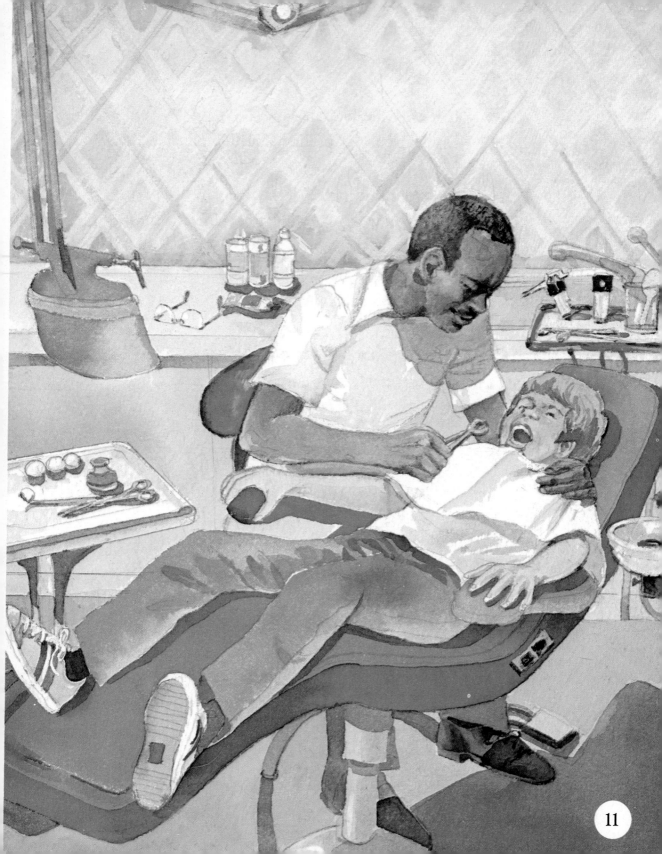

In a way, he had an excuse.

Dr. Wilson was pulling one of Encyclopedia's teeth.

"There!" said Dr. Wilson. He said it cheerfully, as if he were handing Encyclopedia an ice cream cone instead of a tooth.

"Ugh!" said Encyclopedia.

Dr. Wilson said, "All right. Hop down from the chair."

Encyclopedia hopped down and put the tooth in his pocket. He was going to give it to Charlie Stewart, who collected teeth and kept them in a flowered cookie jar.

Encyclopedia went into the waiting room. The chair on which he had left Sally's roller skates was empty!

He looked behind the chair. He dropped to his knees and looked under the chair.

"The skates—they're gone!" he exclaimed.

"Are you sure you brought them with you?" asked Dr. Wilson.

"I'm sure," answered Encyclopedia. "They were broken. I fixed them last night for my partner, Sally Kimball. I was going to take them over to her house on my way home from your office."

Dr. Wilson shook his head sadly. "I'm afraid you will never get them back."

But Dr. Wilson knew nothing about detective work. Encyclopedia liked the dentist, though he felt that Vivian was a better first name for a woman than a man.

"I'll find the skates," said the boy detective. He spoke with certainty. But he felt no such thing. What he felt was the blow to his pride; it hurt worse than his jaw. Imagine a detective being robbed!

In the corridor outside Dr. Wilson's office, Encyclopedia leaned against the wall. He closed his eyes and did some deep thinking.

Dr. Wilson's office was on the ground floor of the new Medical Building. The building had three floors and fifteen offices. All the offices were used by doctors or dentists.

What if the thief had followed him into the building in order to steal the skates? Then the case was closed. "I could spend the rest of my life looking through closets, school lockers, and garages all over Idaville," Encyclopedia thought.

But suppose the thief had simply come into the building to see a doctor. Suppose, on his way in, he had noticed a boy carrying a pair of roller skates. Well, that was something else!

Encyclopedia reasoned further. "The thief could be a grown-up, a boy, or a girl."

He ruled out a grown-up. First, because it was unlikely that a grown-up would steal an old pair of small skates. Second, because a grown-up would be too hard to catch. Too many men and women went in and out of the Medical Building every hour.

"I'll have to act on the idea that the thief is a boy or a girl," he decided. "It's a long chance, but the only one I have."

He opened his eyes. The case called for plain, old-fashioned police leg work!

Encyclopedia began on the ground floor. He asked the same question in every office: "Were any boys or girls here to see the doctor this morning?"

The answer was the same in every office: "No."

Things looked hopeless. But on the top floor he finally got a lead. The nurse in room 301 told him a boy named Billy Haggerty had been there this morning to have a sprained wrist treated.

Encyclopedia asked in the last two offices— just to be sure. Neither doctor had treated children that morning.

Billy Haggerty became suspect number one!

Encyclopedia got Billy Haggerty's address from the nurse in room 301. He hurried back to Dr. Wilson's office to use the telephone. He called Sally. He told her to meet him in front of the Haggertys' house in half an hour.

"We may have some rough going ahead of us," he warned.

But Billy Haggerty turned out to be only an inch taller than Encyclopedia, and shorter than Sally.

Billy drew himself up to his full height at Encyclopedia's first question: "Were you in Dr. Vivian Wilson's office this morning?"

"Naw," snapped Billy. "I don't know any Dr. Wilson."

"You didn't ask anyone about Dr. Wilson?" put in Sally.

"I never heard of him before you spoke his name," said Billy.

"Then you went straight to your own doctor on the third floor?" said Encyclopedia.

"Yeah. Dr. Stanton in room 301. What's it to you?"

"Dr. Wilson's office is down the hall from both the stairs and the elevator," said Encyclopedia thoughtfully. "You wouldn't pass his office going up or coming down."

"I don't know where his office is, and I don't care," said Billy. "It's none of your business where I was."

"We just want to be sure you weren't in Dr. Vivian Wilson's office this morning. That's all," said Sally.

"Well, I wasn't. I had a sprained wrist, not a toothache. So why should I go near his office?" demanded Billy. "I don't like snoopers. What are you after?"

"A pair of roller skates," said Encyclopedia.
"Do you mind returning them? You've given
yourself away."
WHAT GAVE BILLY AWAY?

Solution to
"The Case of the Missing Roller Skates"

Billy Haggerty said that he had never heard of Dr. Vivian Wilson and that he didn't know where his office was. But he knew too much about him.

He knew that Dr. Vivian Wilson was (1) a man, not a woman; and (2) a dentist, not a doctor.

When he was tripped by his fibs, Billy returned the roller skates to Sally.

Think about the story. Finish the chart on page 9. Then answer the questions.

1. Use your chart and think about the steps Encyclopedia takes. Which step is the beginning of his leg work? Where does he begin?

2. Use your chart. Why does Billy Haggerty become a suspect? During which step does Encyclopedia finally decide the thief is Billy?

3. This story is part of a unit about challenges to be met and problems to be solved. What challenge does the writer give the reader of this selection?

4. How can a careful reader solve the mystery at the same time as Encyclopedia?

5. When Encyclopedia and Sally talk to Billy, how does Billy behave? How do Billy's actions and appearance make us think that he is dishonest?

6. What finally gives Billy's dishonesty away?

7. What other clues might the writer or artist have given to tell us the type of person Billy is?

George Washington felt that honesty was very important in a person. He once said, "...honesty is always the best policy." Talk about what makes someone honest. Ask questions about what your classmates say. Talk about the answers.

Focusing on "An Eskimo Birthday"

Think and Read

▶ Talk about a time you had special plans that were ruined by the weather. Listen to your classmates' experiences. Ask questions about what they say.

▶ Read the title of the story and look at the picture on page 22. Think about what you know about weather changing people's plans.
  ● What does the picture tell us about the weather?
  ● What effect might the weather have on someone's birthday plans?

▶ Get ready to read a story about a girl's special day. As you read, think about the problems Eeka and her family face. Think about how you would complete this chart.

Characters' Problems	
Problems Eeka Faces	Problems Eeka's Family Faces

Now turn the page and read "An Eskimo Birthday." Then you will talk about giving things up for others.

An Eskimo Birthday

A story by Tom D. Robinson

Illustrated by Sandy Rabinowitz

The Eskimo people live in a climate where it is below the freezing point for most of the year. Danger and death have been part of the Eskimos' daily life. Now that there are snowmobiles as well as dog teams, houses instead of igloos, electric lights, and stores, Eskimo life has changed. Still, many of the old people keep to the old ways while the young take on the new.

The strong wind that had brought the storm shook the windows of the little school with each gust. Often even the lights from the closest houses winked, then disappeared as swirls of snow were thrown against the side of the building.

Eeka kept looking, first at the storm, then at the clock above the blackboard. The hands seemed to be held back by giant weights. Only two-thirty—another whole hour to go! Oh, and it was such a special day! "My birthday," she muttered to herself, as she hit her desk softly with her clenched fist.

Eeka had so hoped everything would go perfectly. It had been calm when her father had gone out to check his traps early in the morning. Her mother was home cooking a big meal for the party that night, and then there was the beautiful new parka her mother had sewn, complete but for the fur ruff and trimming.

The trapping season had been a poor one, but there was always the chance that this time, especially this time, her father would have luck and find some fox in his traps so the parka could be finished. Now the storm that had completely covered the village with snow took that slim chance away. Eeka sighed and stared out at the darkness caused by the storm and lack of winter sun.

Just then, the door to the classroom opened. The principal came in and whispered something to Eeka's teacher, and when he left, she quietly asked the children to listen.

"Because the storm seems to be getting worse, we're dismissing school early. Many of your parents are out in the hall, waiting to take you home. If your parents are not there, please be careful when you leave. And," she added, "you fifth graders make sure and take home any little ones who live close to you."

Eeka gave a squeal of delight. She threw her books into her desk and went running to the door.

"Eeka! Eeka!" called her teacher. "Slow down before you run over somebody."

Eeka slowed to a quick walk, while one of the other students explained, "It's her birthday and her mother is cooking for her. That's why she's in a hurry."

The teacher was smiling. "Well, happy birthday, Eeka, but save some energy for the walk home! I'd like to see you in one piece for your party."

Out in the corridor, Eeka found her first-grade cousin waiting for her by the coat hooks. Eeka slipped her old parka over her head, pulled the hood up tight around her face, and thrust her hands into her mittens.

Between the wind and her slippery mukluks, it took all of Eeka's strength to get the school door open. Once outside, the girls were blown sideways several feet by a strong gust before they could regain their balance.

When they were headed in the right direction, they both put their heads down and away from the wind that raged against their sides. Eeka looked up only to check that she was going the right way. Each time, the stinging blasts of snow made her forehead ache with cold.

Neither girl spoke. They would have had to shout to have been heard above the wind, and walking up and down the quickly forming drifts didn't leave much breath for talking. Once in a while, Eeka caught the glimmer of a light from one of the houses. Between that and having walked this way hundreds of times before, she was able to keep on a fairly straight line home.

Eeka's cousin lived right next door to her, so, when they got near their houses, Eeka just let go of the little girl's hand, and she slid down the small drift between the two buildings, stopping with a bump against the storm porch of her house. Her cousin disappeared inside her door.

Eeka looked for her father's snow machine, but it wasn't there. She stood looking past her house in the direction she knew her father had gone, and wondered how he could ever find his way home in this weather.

Pulling a hand out of one of her mittens, she placed it over her nose to warm it up. With the other hand, she pushed the door open and entered the storm porch.

Inside the long, narrow building, Eeka carefully brushed all the fine snow from her parka and pants. The light from the single, bare bulb on the ceiling made scary shadows out of all her father's hunting gear that hung on the walls. Close by the inside door was a box which housed a female dog curled around her four new puppies. Eeka knelt down and let the mother lick her hand. It was a bad time for the pups to be born, these cold months, but her father wanted to build his team back up. His snow machine was old and a new one just cost too much. Eeka gave each puppy a pat.

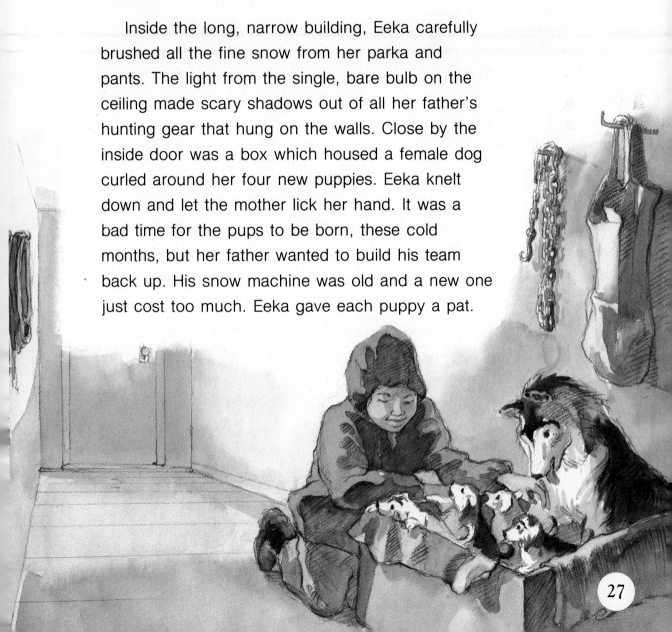

Eeka was greeted by the smell of freshly baked pies and cakes as she entered the house, and a loud screech from her little brother. On seeing her, he threw his bottle over the side of the crib and held out his arms to be picked up. Eeka's mother was bustling about the stove. Bending down for a hug, she said, "Happy birthday, little one."

Eeka walked into the only other room of the house, the bedroom she shared with her mother and father. She put her parka on her bed. On her parents' bed lay the new parka her mother had sewn, a beautiful, dark blue velveteen. There was no telling now when the parka would be done. It seemed enough just to hope her father would make it home all right.

Eeka heard her brother screech again; so she
turned with a sigh and went back into the main
room to pick him up. Her grandfather was sitting
on the edge of his bed in the corner next to the
oil stove. He was slowly stripping bits of baleen to
use in making the shiny, black baskets he sold at
the store. They were small, but they brought a
good price when sold at the right time to the right
people.

He raised his head and looked at Eeka, his
white hair making his wrinkled, brown face seem
even darker. Then he looked at the clock.

"Did they let you out early because it's your
birthday?" he asked with a smile. His voice was
almost a whisper. "Schools sure have changed."

Eeka laughed as she sat down and began to
bounce her brother on her knees. The warmth was
beginning to return to her cheeks. "Not because
of my birthday, Apah. Because of the storm."

"I remember coming home from Sunday school
once, when I was very little," her grandfather
began slowly. He had put his knife down and was
looking toward the window. "It was away from
town—you know the place—up toward the little
lagoon. Anyway, it was stormy like this, and we
were trying to follow the row of whale bones back
to the village. Somehow we got lost and wandered,
it seemed like for hours."

Eeka had heard most of her grandfather's stories, including this one, many times before, but they seemed to get better and better. When other old people came by to visit, they would talk with Grandfather about the way things were in the past. They usually spoke in Eskimo, so Eeka would sit close to her mother who would tell her everything that was being said.

"At first it was fun and then we got scared," Grandfather went on. "We stopped, and some of us started to cry while some of us started to pray. Suddenly, the clouds began to lift toward the south and the wind slowed down. We hadn't noticed the wind when we left the church, or we could have used it as a guide. We were way over on the north beach, almost out on the sea ice. People were looking all over for us. We never knew if it was our praying or our parents' shouting that drove the storm away."

"Well," laughed Eeka's mother, "I'm glad I don't have to worry about Eeka like Grandmother had to worry about you! She would take notice of the wind direction when going out in a storm."

Grandfather chuckled. "I guess children these days are a lot smarter in some things than we were. But," he added, "I'm not sure school gives them all the answers." His eyes were shining.

"It's Eeka's father I'm worried about," Eeka's mother said softly, as she began to dress the baby. A little frown crossed her face as she spoke. "We'd better hurry, Eeka, if we're going to get those things at the store for tonight. And bring the five-gallon can and the little sled so we can get some stove oil." She slipped the baby up under the back of her parka where he would ride safe and warm. Eeka put on her parka and went out to tie the can onto the sled.

The wind was at their backs as they walked to the store. Now and then, an extra strong gust would push them ahead, making them run for a few steps until they regained their balance. The light from a snow machine, or the outline of another figure, would appear close by them, then dissolve back into the snow and darkness. It wasn't as cold walking with the wind, but still Eeka and her mother were happy to see the lights of the new store and the warmth it offered.

Everyone greeted them when they got inside, most people calling out happy birthday to Eeka and kidding her about getting old. Eeka's mother took the baby out from inside her parka. She placed him in the shopping cart, which Eeka began pushing, following her mother up and down the aisles.

As they moved down the back row of the
store, past the hardware, snow machine parts, and
rifles, Eeka and her mother came to the corner
where the furs hung. Eeka stared at the five fox
skins, all of them small and stained yellow with the
oil of the seals the foxes had feasted on. Her
mother walked over and looked at each one.

"They're too expensive, Eeka, and not nearly
good enough for your parka. There were two
others, big and pure white, but they were even
more money. Perhaps your father will bring some
home from his traps."

"It is probably too stormy for him to find his
traps," offered Eeka. "I'll just be glad for him to
get home."

As they walked up to the cash register, Eeka was again teased about its being her "special" day. She blushed and turned away, but she couldn't hide her smile.

The men sitting on kegs and piles of rope near the check-out counter asked Eeka's mother many questions in Eskimo about Eeka's father—when he had left, the direction he had gone, how much gas he had with him, if he had a stove and a tent. Eeka wished at that moment that she'd listened more closely to her grandfather. He had tried to get her to speak Eskimo when she was younger, but she never seemed to have the time. And now, as the men spoke to each other in quiet tones, Eeka understood only that they were discussing a search party.

It seemed impossible to Eeka that in this great, white country one small man, also dressed in white, could be found in such a storm. How she wished he had never gone—and for her!

"Don't worry, little Eeka," her favorite uncle said, putting his big arm around her shoulders. "If your father's not back soon, we will go out and get him. We won't let him miss your birthday party." He smiled down at her, and Eeka began to feel much better.

The walk home was horrible! The wind that had
pushed them over to the store now blew directly in
their faces, some gusts making them stop completely. Both Eeka and her mother put their heads
down, not daring to look up. Her mother pulled
the sled, heavy with the stove oil and the fish.
Eeka carried the rest of the things in a sack
clutched tightly to her chest so it wouldn't blow
away. Many times they turned their backs to the
wind, resting and warming their noses and cheeks
with a bare hand.

Whenever they did glance up to get their directions, the snow flew in their faces and made it
almost impossible to see. As Eeka had done when
coming home from school, they used drifts, oil
drums, dog stakes, and the brief flicker of the light
from a house to guide them.

Finally, when Eeka thought she was as cold as she could get, she saw the familiar shape of her house just ahead. And there, outside the little house, was her father—unloading caribou from his sled. He was home safe! Eeka nearly fell over a drift as she ran ahead to greet him.

Eeka's father had many things to do before he could finally come inside and warm up. First, he carried in a large piece of meat and placed it by the stove to thaw out so it could be used in caribou soup that evening. Then he and Grand-father had to unload the sled and cover the snow

machine. Finally, there was the oil to put in the drum alongside the house, and the four older dogs to be fed. Only then was he able to come in and get the hot cup of coffee that would start the wonderful heat flowing back into his body.

All this time, Eeka helped her mother unpack their groceries, anxiously waiting for a chance to see if her father had trapped a fox. When everything was put away, she crowded near him, but she couldn't bring herself to ask.

Then Eeka's father spoke to her.

"All my traps were covered by the snow, Eeka," her father said. "There was a bit of fur in one trap where a fox had been, but I think a wolverine beat me to him. Maybe he thinks he's found somebody who will feed him and he will return to the trap. The next thing he'll know, he will be a pair of new mittens for you, as punishment for having taken your fox." Eeka tried to smile, but it was hard not to look disappointed.

"Eeka," called her mother, "come and feed your brother. There is much to do before the party and it is almost time for people to come." Eeka was glad to be busy rather than have time to think about something that couldn't be helped. In fact, she was so busy that she was surprised when the door opened and the first of the guests walked in.

By the time all the people had arrived, the last cake had been iced and the caribou soup was done. Eeka and her mother laid a cloth out on the floor and put the food and dishes on it. People could help themselves, and eat either sitting on the floor or on one of the benches at the table.

When Eeka's mother called her to come open her presents, the girls began teasing about what they had brought. Eeka didn't like the idea of standing up in front of all the other people, but she was anxious to see what she had gotten.

Everyone had brought something, either an envelope with a card and money in it, or a present wrapped in a paper sack with a birthday message written across the outside. Eeka's mother insisted that she read every one before she opened it. Some were serious and some, like the message from her uncle, made people laugh until tears ran down their faces.

There were more things than Eeka had ever hoped to get—clothes from the store, a game, a deck of playing cards, a scarf knit by an aunt, a beautiful pair of caribou mukluks from her grandmother, and almost ten dollars from the envelopes.

Eeka was gladly just about to give up her place as the center of attention, when one of the women walked out of the bedroom and held the new parka up to Eeka.

"Here," she said, "put it on so everyone can
see the fine present your mother has made for you."

Eeka stared at the parka. Without a ruff or trim
it looked anything but nice. It was so lifeless!
Why? thought Eeka. Everything was going so well.
I hate that ugly thing! I hate it! But she blindly
shoved her hands into the sleeves and stood
there, head down, while everyone commented on
what a fine parka it was.

Suddenly, she could stand it no longer. Eeka turned to rush from the room, to take the parka off and hide the tears she knew would come if she had to hear another word.

She almost knocked her grandfather down as she spun around. He had left his place on the bed and had silently made his way to her side. He was holding a sack in his hand, which he gave to Eeka.

"Here," he said quietly. "They aren't very good, but it was all the store would give me for one of my little baskets."

All was silent as Eeka opened the sack and looked inside. Slowly, unable to believe her eyes, she pulled out two of the most beautiful white fox skins she had ever seen. They must have been the ones her mother had spoken of at the store!

Immediately, everyone began talking about what fine skins they were—surely the best taken that year! They were passed from hand to hand, so much so that Eeka feared all the fur would be rubbed off. The women discussed how best to cut them to get the most trim and biggest ruff, while the men talked about their whiteness and who had trapped them.

Grandfather sat on the edge of his bed, holding a cup of tea and looking at the floor. The only sign that he heard the remarks about the skins

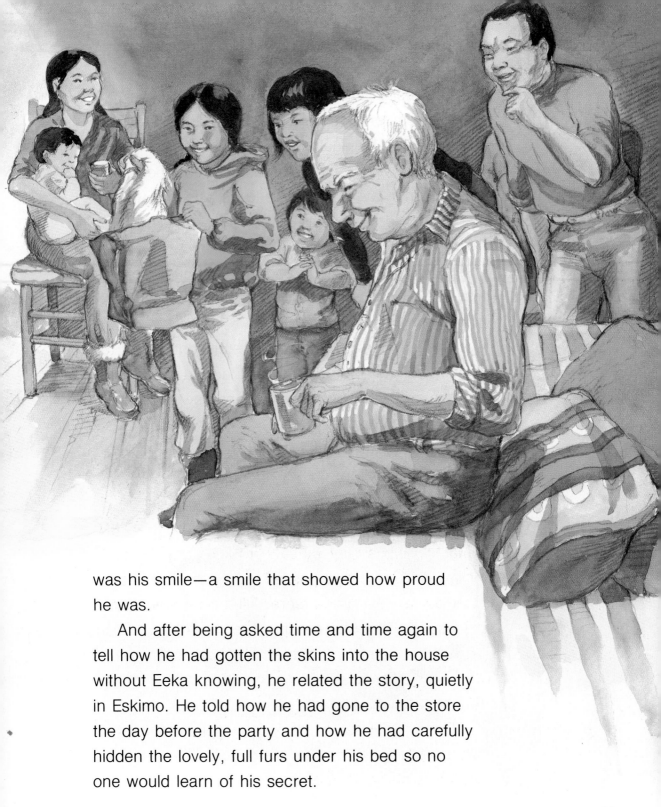

was his smile—a smile that showed how proud
he was.

And after being asked time and time again to
tell how he had gotten the skins into the house
without Eeka knowing, he related the story, quietly
in Eskimo. He told how he had gone to the store
the day before the party and how he had carefully
hidden the lovely, full furs under his bed so no
one would learn of his secret.

The rest of the evening was a blur to Eeka. She remembered holding the fox skins and rubbing the soft fur against her cheek.

On her way to bed, she stopped by where Grandfather lay. He seemed to be asleep, but Eeka knelt down beside him and whispered, "Thank you, Apah. Thank you very much." The old man put out a hand and touched Eeka gently on her head. He was smiling, his eyes closed, when she left him.

The last sound she heard, before drifting off to sleep, was her mother humming an old, old song as she swiftly cut up the skins and sewed them onto the new parka.

Think about the story. Finish the chart on page 21.
Then answer the questions.

1. Use your chart and think about the selection.
   Which of Eeka's problems are the same as the
   family's? Which are different?

2. The selections in this unit are about problems to
   be faced and challenges to be met. Think about
   what you wrote in your chart. What causes most of
   the problems in this story? *The coldness and The snow* *a beach to*

3. What present might Eeka want if she lived on a
   tropical island? What might she want if she lived
   on a mountaintop? Give reasons for your answers.

4. Eeka says, "I'll just be glad for him to get home." *her dad*
   Whom is she thinking about? How does what she
   says show that she is thinking of others before
   herself?

5. How does Eeka really feel about sacrificing, or
   giving up, her furs? How can you tell?

6. How does Grandfather's sacrifice solve Eeka's
   problem? Is this a good solution? Why or why not?

Think and Discuss

WORK IN A GROUP

Talk about a time you gave up something for someone else. Explain how you felt. Tell why you felt that way. Ask questions about what your classmates say.

Focusing on "Meeting Nature's Challenges"

Think and Read

▶ Talk about how climate shaped people's lives in "An Eskimo Birthday." Discuss ways that climate shapes how people live. Ask questions about what your classmates say.

▶ Read the title of the article on page 46. Think about about how climate shapes people's lives.
  - How might nature "challenge" someone?
  - What would you expect this article to be about?

▶ As you read, pay close attention to how people adapt, or change, to live in their surroundings. Think about what you would add to this diagram.

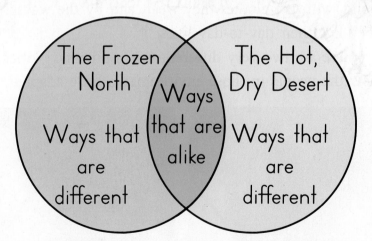

The Frozen North

Ways that are different

Ways that are alike

The Hot, Dry Desert

Ways that are different

Now turn the page and read "Meeting Nature's Challenges." Then you will discuss new ways people think of to live in their surroundings.

Meeting Nature's Challenges

People all around the world live in different *environments,* or surroundings, that affect their lives. Some people live in hot, dry deserts. Some people live on cold, snowy mountains. Some people live near hot, wet jungles. Some people live near cool, dry forests. In many environments, the weather changes with the seasons: warm in the summer, cold in the winter.

People have learned to *adapt,* or learn a way of life that suits their different environments. People can adapt to their environments with the houses they build, with the clothes they wear, and by the ways they live their day-to-day lives.

Here are two very different environments. Notice how the people in those environments have adapted.

The Frozen North

This is northern Alaska, a land of challenge. Northern Alaska is near the Arctic Circle and the North Pole. Life here is not easy. Winters are eight or nine months long. They are dark and bitterly cold. In the winter, the sun shines only an hour or two each day, and temperatures drop to about $-60°F$.

Temperatures rise above freezing ($32°F$) for only two or three months of the year. These two or three summer months are cool, even though the sun almost never sets. During these months, the top one or two feet of soil may thaw. Then mosses, shrubs, weeds, and wildflowers grow. The ground underneath, however, stays frozen all year round and cannot be plowed for farming.

Eskimos, or *Inuit* (IN·oo·it) as they call themselves, have lived in this harsh environment for thousands of years. They can live here because they have found ways to meet the problems of life in the Arctic.

Look at the Eskimo winter house on page 48. It has thick earth walls that keep in warm air and keep

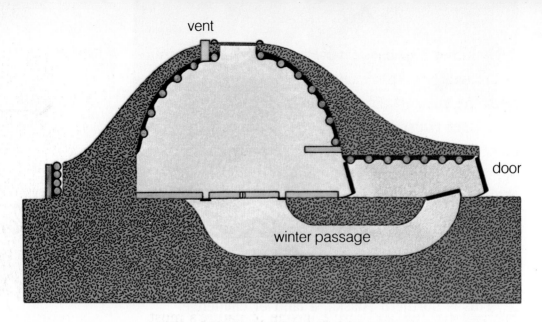

vent

door

winter passage

out cold air. The house has an opening, or *vent*, in the ceiling. The door is lower than the floor of the house and is separated from the house by a long, underground tunnel.

The Eskimos heat their houses with oil lamps. Two or three lamps can heat a house to 80° or 90°F. The door stays open, even in the coldest weather. Cold air collects in the underground tunnel. However, cold air is heavier than warm air, so the cold air in the tunnel cannot flow into the warm air in the house unless the Eskimos open the vent in the ceiling.

Once the vent in the ceiling is opened, the warm air in the room rises and flows outside. This leaves room for the cold air from the tunnel to come in and cool the house.

When the house has been cooled as much as the Eskimos want, they close the vent. The warm air settles back down into the house, stopping the cold air from the tunnel.

Eskimos also have learned to adapt their clothing to the weather. In winter they wear *two* suits made from the skins of the *caribou* (KAR·uh·boo), the great deer that roam the Arctic. Eskimos wear the inner suit with the fur next to the body and the outer suit with the fur facing out. Body heat is trapped next to the body and between the two suits. Eskimo boots are sewn from caribou skins, too. The boots are so watertight that they can be blown up like balloons!

By adapting their homes and their clothing, Eskimos can live and thrive in one of nature's most challenging environments.

The Hot, Dry Desert

Far from Alaska lies the land of North Africa. The North African environment is quite different from that of northern Alaska, yet its climate is just as harsh. North Africa contains the world's largest desert–the *Sahara* (suh·HAR·uh), which is more than three million square miles in size.

The Sahara has mountains, rocky plateaus (pla·TOHZ), treeless plains, and sandy wasteland. The Sahara has less than eight inches of rain every year. Temperatures during the day are very hot, as high as 110°F. However, the desert sand does not hold the heat. When the sun sets, the desert becomes cool.

The problems faced by the North Africans living in the hot desert are different from those of the Eskimos living in the cold Arctic. Yet the desert people have adapted to their environment in ways much like the Arctic people have adapted to theirs.

Like the Eskimos, the people of the Sahara build houses with thick walls. In the desert, thick walls help keep heat *out* during the hot days and *in* during the cold nights. Mostly, though, their homes protect the North Africans from the scorching heat.

Desert people paint their homes white to reflect the sun's rays. They build houses close together to shade one another, and they plant trees for even more shade. Under their homes, they dig cool cellars in which they often stay during the hottest times of the year.

Desert people also use their clothing for protection from the heat. People of the Sahara wrap themselves up much like the Eskimos do. However, the Eskimos wrap themselves up to stay warm, while the desert people wrap themselves up to stay cool. The desert people's robes, turbans, and veils keep the sun and wind from reaching their bodies. Because of the harsh desert heat and dryness, desert people must also protect themselves from *dehydration* (DEE·hy·DRAY·shuhn), or loss of water from the body. They must always be near water or carry it with them when they travel.

Nature's Challenge

The hot Sahara and the cold Arctic are only two of the many environments in which the people of the Earth live and make homes. Yet as different as one environment is from the other, people have found ways to adapt. A difficult environment is nature's challenge—to be met and overcome.

Think about the article. Finish the diagram on page 45. Then answer the questions.

1. Use your diagram. In what ways are the problems of living in the frozen north like those of living in the hot, dry desert?

2. Use your diagram. Why can people live in places as different as the Arctic and the desert?

3. Why do Eskimos hunt instead of farming?

4. Why do both Arctic and desert dwellers build their homes with thick walls?

5. Would you expect someone who lives in the Arctic to paint his or her house white? Why or why not?

6. How would you solve the problem of dehydration in the desert?

7. What other problems besides heat and cold might make people adapt their housing?

8. Why does the writer call difficult environments "nature's challenge"? How does an article with this title fit into a unit about problems to be solved?

Think and Discuss

Ask classmates about inventions that have helped people adapt to your own environment. Make a list. Some possibilities are *air conditioning*, *down coats*, and *subways*. Work with your classmates to put the list in order of importance.

Focusing on "It Pays to Advertise"

▶ Talk about a time you needed to earn money to buy something special. Listen to what your classmates say. Ask questions.

▶ Look at the title and the picture on page 54. Read the first paragraph on page 55. Think about what you know about people wanting to earn money.
  ● Which person wants to earn money to buy something special? How do you know?
  ● How might Benjy learn that "it pays to advertise"?

▶ Get ready to read about how Benjy tries to solve his problem. As you read the story, think about why Benjy is working. Think about what you would add to this diagram.

"It Pays to Advertise"

Introduction	Development	Conclusion
Problem	Steps	Solution

Now turn the page and read "It Pays to Advertise." Then you will talk about working hard.

IT PAYS TO ADVERTISE

From the story *Benjy in Business* by Jean Van Leeuwen
Illustrated by Ted Carr

*More than anything else, nine-year-old Benjy
wanted a Clyde Johnson catcher's mitt. But how was
he going to get it?*

*Benjy's parents suggest that he work for the
money, so Benjy goes into business for the summer.
His first job—taking care of his baby sister—is too
tiring, and Benjy doesn't feel he has the strength to
take care of her long enough to earn the money he
needs. His second business venture—washing cars—is
a failure. Not only do Benjy and his friend Jason not
get much business, but it rains the entire afternoon.
Discouraged, Benjy sits down to the table with his
mother to find a solution. He just has to have that
catcher's mitt!*

"Hot chocolate?" said his mother. "In the middle
of summer?"

Benjy watched the water roll from his hair down
his face to his shirt and then drip from his shorts
onto the kitchen floor. "Please?" he said.

"Well, all right," said his mother. "But get out of these clothes quickly before we have to bail out the kitchen."

When Benjy got back, she was just pouring the hot chocolate into his mug. "One marshmallow or two?" she asked.

"Two," said Benjy.

"Silly question," said his mother, smiling. She sat down across from him at the table. "Well, how did the car-wash business work out?"

"Terrible," said Benjy.

"That bad?" said his mother.

Benjy nodded. It was peaceful sitting in the kitchen drinking hot chocolate with the rain pouring down outside. And with just his mother for a change. Usually his sister was there, too, banging on her tray with her shoe or babbling away in her strange language. It was past time for her to be up from her nap—she must have overslept. Benjy told his mother about sitting by the mailbox for hours while all the cars went by without stopping, and keeping on adding things to his sign, and how when he finally got his first customer, it started to rain.

"That was bad luck about the rain," said his mother.

"It was bad luck about the whole day," said Benjy.

"What do you think went wrong?" asked his mother.

Benjy shrugged. "I guess no one wanted their car washed."

"Well," said his mother, "not enough people, anyway. Remember what your father said? You have to have something to sell that people want to buy." She looked out the window thoughtfully. "One other thing you might keep in mind if you want to be a businessman. People can't buy your service unless they know about it. You have to advertise."

"You mean like on TV and in the newspaper?" said Benjy.

"Not quite like that," said his mother. "But if you just have a sign on the mailbox, only people who happen to pass your mailbox will see it."

"I could make more signs," said Benjy. "And put them up on other roads, like they do for garage sales."

"That's what I mean," said his mother. "Then you can attract customers who don't live on our street."

"I could even put a sign on Route One Seventy-one," said Benjy.

"Well, maybe not there," said his mother. "Cars on the highway are usually going too fast to stop. Anyway, that's a suggestion if you decide to go into business again. It pays to advertise."

"Right," said Benjy.

Benjy didn't go into business again the next day. He thought he needed some time off. Besides, it was still raining.

He fished around under his bed and in his closet and a few other places and found all his baseball cards. Using two shoeboxes, he separated them into

this year's and last year's. Then he sorted this year's cards into piles according to teams and put rubber bands around them. That took most of the day. After that he copied Clyde Johnson's picture from last year's card, colored it with his colored pencils, and put it up on his bulletin board.

Looking at the picture made him think about the mitt again. He had to get it, and soon. Otherwise his

baseball career would never take off. But he still
needed $20.43. How was he ever going to get it?

The next morning Benjy went over to see Jason.
He was bound to have some ideas. Not that all of his
ideas were terrific, but he always had a lot of them.

"I've got it!" said Jason when he and Benjy were
hanging by their knees from the climbing bars of
Jason's swing set. "A worm farm!"

59

"A *worm* farm?" They were looking at the world upside down, with the worms on top. Something must have gotten jumbled inside Jason's brain.

"I'm not kidding," said Jason. "I read about it in a book. This kid digs up his backyard and makes pits and raises worms to sell. And he makes a fortune."

Benjy could just see his mother's face if he told her he was going to have a worm farm. He could also see his father's face if he told him he was going to dig pits in the backyard. This wasn't one of Jason's better ideas.

"It'll never fly," Benjy told him.

Jason let go with his hands and swung so his hair just brushed the ground.

"How about this?" he said, smiling upside down. "We open a gym in my basement, and we charge people to join. Like a health club. And they get to use my brother's barbells and his punching bag and all that stuff."

Too much blood must be rushing to Jason's head.

"Use your brother's stuff?" said Benjy. "Your brother won't even let *you* use his stuff."

"Oh, yeah," said Jason. "I forgot."

Maybe he'd do better right side up. Benjy did a quick skin-the-cat and went to sit in the shade.

Jason flopped down next to him. "Sure is hot," he said.

"The thing of it is," said Benjy, "that you have to have something to sell that people want to buy."

"Right," said Jason.

"If you were a customer, what would you like to buy?" asked Benjy.

"Right now," said Jason, "I'd like to buy a drink."

Benjy looked at him. Jason had done it again. He'd always known he could count on him for ideas.

"That's it," said Benjy.

"It is?" said Jason.

"Sure," said Benjy. "We can sell lemonade."

"Now, that is a good idea," said Jason.

They made six signs on big pieces of cardboard,
all with red arrows saying LEMONADE THIS WAY, and
put them up on nearby corners. The seventh sign
said LEMONADE HERE—15¢ A CUP. They stuck that
one on the mailbox. Benjy's mother gave them a
pitcher of lemonade and a stack of paper cups. She
let them use an old card table for a lemonade stand,
and Benjy got two folding chairs from the garage.

He sat down in one—just as Charlie Fryhoffer
drove by without even looking.

"Oh, no," groaned Benjy. "This better not be like
last time."

But it wasn't. In the first ten minutes three cars
stopped. One was Mrs. Bolton with her two little
kids and their two friends. She bought five cups. A
man from Adams Air Conditioning bought two cups.
And another woman in a station wagon with three
kids bought four cups. "I saw your sign over on
Laurel Lane," she said. "A cup of lemonade hits the
spot on a day like this."

As she drove away Jason stuck out his hand. "Congratulations, old pal," he said. "You're going to rake in a fortune."

Benjy grinned. "Same to you. It was your idea."

Money was jingling in his pocket. And the pitcher of lemonade was nearly empty. Already.

Benjy went to the house to get more.

"Already?" said his mother. "Business must be good."

"I'm going to rake in a fortune," he told her.

"In that case," said his mother, "you can pay me back for the lemonade. That's how it's done in business, you know. You have to invest money to make money."

"No problem," said Benjy. "I'll pay you when we close up the stand."

The second pitcher went fast too. And the third. Just about everyone on Benjy's street stopped at the lemonade stand. Mrs. Parkinson and a friend of hers and Mrs. Rosedale and Alex Crowley's mother and sister. And the mailman and the man who came to read the electric meters. And a lot of people Benjy had never seen before.

"Those signs are really working," said Jason.

"It pays to advertise," said Benjy.

His pockets were overflowing with money now. He needed a cash register. When he went to get the fourth pitcher of lemonade, he brought back one of his baseball-card shoeboxes. He dumped all the money into it.

"Wow!" said Jason. "It looks like you get your mitt tomorrow."

"Maybe," said Benjy.

He started counting it. But he'd only gotten to $2.50 when another car stopped, its brakes screeching.

Jason nudged him. "Look who finally decided to give us a break."

Benjy looked up. It was Charlie Fryhoffer.

"You guys got the right idea," he said, whipping out a comb and working over his hair. It was so long, Benjy didn't know how he could see where he was driving. He handed Charlie a cup of lemonade and Charlie drank it in one gulp and held out the cup for a refill. Then he tossed Benjy two quarters. "Keep the change," he said. And he took off down the road, his car clanking like a lawn mower.

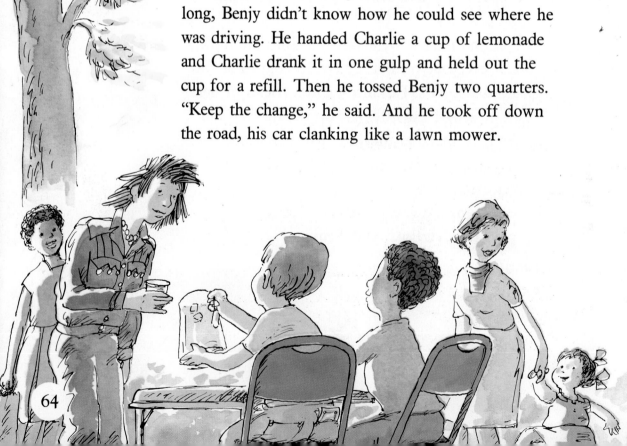

"One of these days," said Jason, "his engine's
going to fall out right in the middle of the road."

"If he doesn't drive into a tree first," said Benjy.

After Charlie Fryhoffer things quieted down a
little. It was getting late in the afternoon and it
wasn't as hot. Mrs. Bolton stopped again, but only to
ask how they were doing. A man in a tan delivery
van stopped and bought one cup. And then no one.

"Want to call it a day?" Jason asked.

"Not yet," said Benjy. "I've got to sell this last
pitcher. I'm paying my mother for it."

"How about having a catch while we're waiting?"
Jason suggested.

That sounded good to Benjy. He was tired of sitting in the folding chair. His legs felt like they were falling asleep.

Benjy got his mitt and a tennis ball. He let Jason use the old catcher's mitt that used to belong to his father. They took turns pitching a few.

Jason was wild. He walked two batters and then made a wild pitch.

But Benjy struck out the side. His fastball zipped right down the middle, and his change-up got the outside corner of the plate. Even his curve ball seemed to be curving a little.

"Nice throwing," said Jason.

"Thanks," said Benjy. There was a possibility that he might be a pitcher when he grew up instead of an outfielder. If he could just learn to throw a slider.

Then they gave each other high fly balls.

It was the last of the ninth and the Yankees were ahead, 1–0, on a homer by Clyde Johnson. But the Red Sox were threatening. They had two men on and two out and their cleanup hitter, Jim Barker, stepping up to the plate.

He swung on the first pitch. And it was a long fly ball out to deep centerfield. Clyde Johnson was racing back. Could he get there in time? He was all the way back, up against the centerfield wall. He leaped high in the air.

And he missed. Benjy tripped on a tree root and fell flat on his back. He heard a strange *clunk*. And then he heard Jason laughing.

Benjy looked up. There was the yellow tennis
ball, in the pitcher of lemonade.

"Nice catch," said Jason.

"Nice throw," said Benjy. He picked himself up.
"Well," he said, "we may as well call it a day."

Jason took the signs down and Benjy put everything away inside. Then they went up to Benjy's
room to count the money in the shoebox. It came
to $7.30.

"Looks like you don't get your mitt tomorrow,"
said Jason.

"No," said Benjy. "But at least I'm starting to get
someplace."

He handed Jason a dollar.

"What's that for?" asked Jason.

"For helping," said Benjy. "A businessman has to
pay his employees, you know."

He went downstairs to find his mother.

"How much do I owe you for the lemonade?" he asked.

"Well, it was fifty-nine cents a can and you used four cans," she said. "But I'll throw in the first one free. That comes to—let's see—a dollar seventy-seven."

Benjy counted out the money.

"Thanks," said his mother.

"Thanks for the free can," said Benjy.

He went back upstairs and counted what was left in the shoebox. Now it came to $4.53. Benjy stuffed it all into his monkey bank. Then he got his piece of paper and did some subtraction. Twenty dollars and forty-three cents minus $4.53 was $15.90. He still had $15.90 to go.

Benjy sighed. "Making money sure is tough work," he said to Jason.

Jason was looking through Benjy's baseball cards. "Yeah," he said. "Spending it is a lot easier." Then he looked up. "You know what you've got to do, Benjy? Start thinking big. Forget about stuff like lemonade, fifteen cents a cup. You need to go for big money."

Benjy nodded. That's what he needed, all right. Big money. "But what kind of business can a kid go into to make big money?" he asked.

"I don't know yet," said Jason. "But don't worry, I'll think of something. Hey, Benjy, want to trade your Jose Lopez? I'll give you two all-stars."

"No way," said Benjy.

Think about the story. Finish the diagram on page 53. Then answer the questions.

Finish the diagram on page 53.

1. As the story begins, what has Benjy already done to earn money? What problems has he run into?

2. Look at your diagram. Do you think Benjy takes the correct steps to solve his problem? What would you do differently?

3. What does Benjy's mother mean when she says, "It pays to advertise"?

4. What is the first sign the boys get that their advertising is working?

5. Pretend you are Benjy. Tell your mother what lessons you have learned by the end of the story.

6. This story is part of a unit about problems to be faced and challenges to be met. How does this selection fit into this unit?

Benjy and Jason both worked hard. Talk about reasons for working hard. Ask questions about what your classmates say. Make a list of five reasons. Put them in order of importance.

Think and Discuss

WORK IN A GROUP

69

TALKING ABOUT THE SELECTIONS

You have read these selections.

Arithmetic
Pudden Tame
Where R U?
The Case of the Missing Roller Skates
An Eskimo Birthday
Meeting Nature's Challenges
It Pays to Advertise

Talk about the selections you have read. Consider how the ideas and characters are alike and different. Talk about the theme.

1. How are Encyclopedia Brown and Benjy alike? How are they different?

2. Do you think Eeka's grandfather is more like Benjy or more like Encyclopedia Brown? Tell why you think as you do.

3. In which selections does bad weather create problems for the characters? Explain your answers.

4. Which character do you think has the most difficult problem to solve? Why?

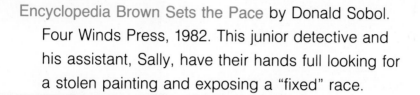

BOOKSHELF

Encyclopedia Brown Sets the Pace by Donald Sobol. Four Winds Press, 1982. This junior detective and his assistant, Sally, have their hands full looking for a stolen painting and exposing a "fixed" race.

Stories to Solve by Jim Shannon. Greenwillow, 1985. Look sharply and use your common sense. See if you can solve the puzzles in these fourteen folk tales.

A Game of Catch by Helen Cresswell. Macmillan, 1977. During a game of tag in an empty castle gallery, Kate and Hugh hear children's laughter. Kate suspects it came from one of the paintings, but none of her friends or family believe her.

Peter Pitseolak's Escape from Death by Peter Pitseolak. Delacorte, 1978. Peter, an Eskimo and an artist, tells his story of the great danger he and his son faced while stranded on a sheet of ice one night.

Sprout and the Magician by Jennifer Wayne. McGraw-Hill, 1977. The rabbit belonging to Tilly, Sprout's sister, disappears. A magician is Sprout's number one suspect.

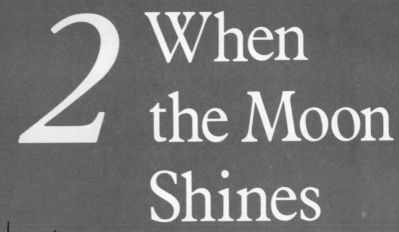

2 When the Moon Shines

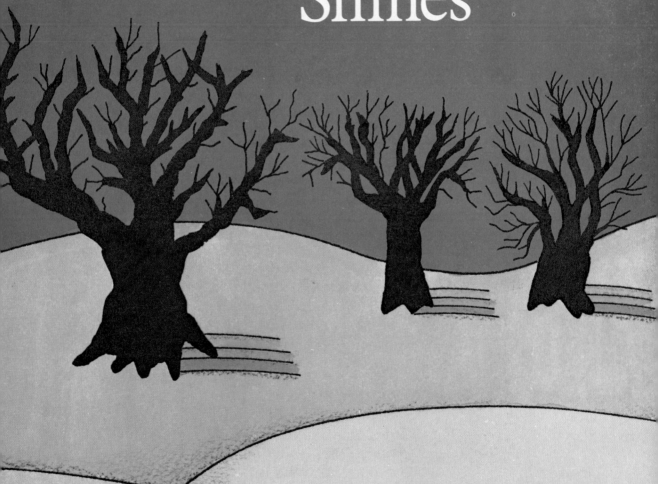

TALKING ABOUT THE THEME

Look at the picture on pages 72 and 73 and read the title.

1. What does the picture make you think of?

2. How does the title fit the picture?

3. Do scary things always frighten people? Why or why not?

4. What are some scary things that you have enjoyed?

5. How do you think the selections in this unit will be alike?

Other Books About Things That Are Not What They Seem

Freaky Friday by Mary Rodgers. Harper & Row, 1972. Annabel wakes up one morning to find that she is in her mother's body.

The Wizard in the Tree by Alexander Lloyd. E.P. Dutton, 1975. A mixed-up wizard has to save the villagers from a wicked squire.

The Girl Who Married a Ghost and Other Tales from the North American Indians collected by Edward S. Curtis and edited by John Bierhorst. Four Winds Press, 1978. These nine tales of weird happenings were handed down through generations of Indian storytellers.

Focusing on "The Ghost in the Attic"

▶ How do you feel when you are in a dark place? On a sheet of paper, quickly write as much as you can. After you have finished, share your ideas with your classmates. Ask questions about what your classmates say.

▶ Read the title and look at the picture on page 76. Think about how you feel about being in a dark place.

- What are the children in the picture doing?
- How do you think the dark attic will be important in this story?

▶ Get ready to read about what happens to the Moffat children when they try to play a trick. As you read, notice how the setting changes. Think about how the changes shape what happens in the rest of the story. Think about how you would complete this chart.

Setting: when and where

↓

Change in Setting	→	What Happens Because of Setting

Now turn the page and read "The Ghost in the Attic." Then you will talk about scary places.

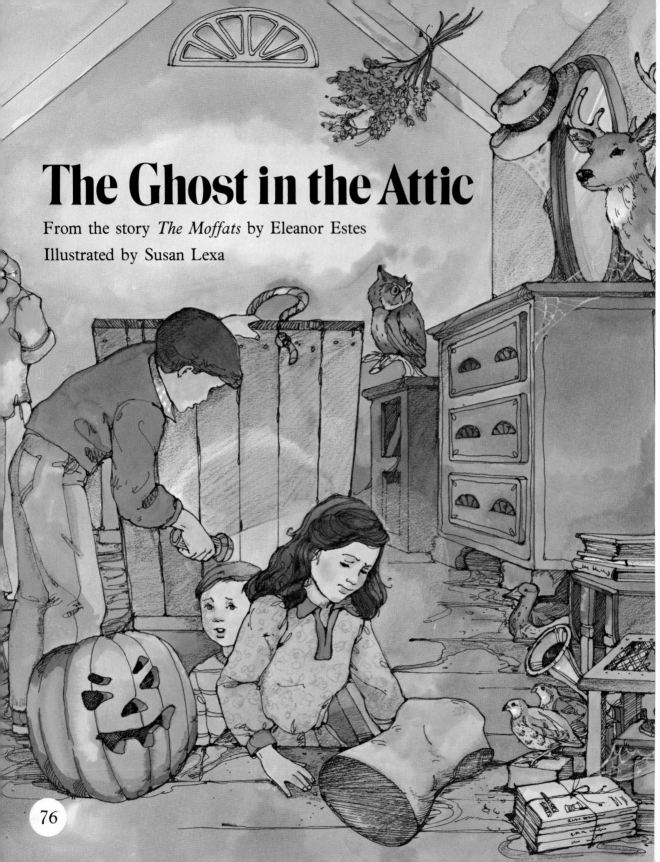

The Ghost in the Attic

From the story *The Moffats* by Eleanor Estes

Illustrated by Susan Lexa

It's Halloween and the Moffat children have told Peter Frost that a ghost is in their attic. Since Peter Frost has played mean tricks on each of them, all of the Moffats want to scare him. Even Catherine-the-cat helps when she gets tangled in the rope attached to the ghost the Moffats have created. As they march to the attic with sheets, a carved pumpkin head, a scooter, and their mother's dressmaking form (Madame-the-bust), Joe, Sylvie, Jane, and Rufus don't realize how frightening their ghost will be.

Slowly the procession made its way out of the Grape Room, into the hall, up the stairs to the second floor. Joe led the way with his pocket flash-light. From the hall upstairs, a stepladder led to the attic which did not have a regular door but a hatch which Joe had to push up with his shoulders. It fell open with a groan and the strange musty smell of the attic greeted them. Joe set the head on the floor and flashed the light down the stepladder so the others could see to climb up.

Sylvie hoisted Madame up before her and climbed in. Then Rufus handed up his scooter and hoisted himself in. As Jane was making her way up, Catherine-the-cat leaped past her and disappeared into the dark recesses of the attic. Jane bit her tongue but managed to keep from screaming. That cat! She was always doing unexpected things behind you.

The four Moffats stood around the entrance, the nearest point to the kitchen, to safety. Joe's tiny flashlight scarcely penetrated the darkness of the attic. But they knew what was up here all right without seeing. Dr. Witty had had many different hobbies. Collecting and stuffing wild animals and birds was one of them. He stored these in the attic in the yellow house. In one corner was a stuffed owl. In another, a stuffed wildcat. And all around were a great many little stuffed partridges and quail. The four children shivered, partly from cold, partly from excitement.

"Oh, let's hurry and get out of this place," said Jane.

They placed the scooter in the corner by the owl. Then they put Madame on the scooter, put the pumpkin head with its ominous, gaping mouth on her headless neck, and draped the sheets about her.

They tied one end of the rope to the scooter and made a loop in the other end in order to be able to pull the ghost around easily. The end of the rope with the loop they placed near the hatchway.

"All right," said Sylvie. "Now let's see how she looks."

They went to the head of the ladder. Joe flashed
his light on Madame—Madame-the-bust no longer,
or Mrs. Shoemaker or Miss Nippon either, but
Madame-the-ghost!

"Phew!" he whistled.

"Boy, oh, boy!" said Rufus.

"Oh," shivered Jane, "come on."

As fast as they could, they pushed the hatch back
in place and hurried helter-skelter to the kitchen
where they warmed their hands over the kitchen fire.

"Boy, oh, boy!" said Rufus again, "what a ghost!"

Then they all put on the most fearful masks that
Sylvie had made for them. And just in the nick of
time too, for here was Peter Frost stamping on the
back porch.

"Hey there, Moffats," he said witheringly. "Where's your old ghost then?"

Oh, his arrogance was insufferable.

"Don't worry," said Sylvie, "you'll see her all right. But you must be quiet."

"Haw-haw," jeered Peter Frost. But he stopped short, for out of the night came a long-drawn howl, a howl of reproach.

Sylvie, Joe, Jane, and Rufus had the same thought. Catherine-the-cat! They had forgotten her up there with the ghost. But Peter Frost! Why, he knew nothing of that of course, and although he was inclined to toss the matter lightly aside, still he blanched visibly when again from some mysterious dark recess of the house came the same wild howl.

The four Moffats knew when to be silent and they were silent now. So was Peter Frost. So was the whole house. It was so silent it began to speak with a thousand voices. When Mama's rocking-chair creaked, Peter Frost looked at it as though he expected to see the ghost sitting right in it. Somewhere a shutter came unfastened and banged against the house. The clock in the sitting-room ticked slowly, painfully, as though it had a lump in its throat, then stopped altogether. Even the Moffats began to feel scared, particularly Rufus. He began to think this whole business on a par with G–R–I–N–D your bones in "Jack and the Beanstalk."

Peter Frost swallowed his breath with a great gulp and said in a voice a trifle less jeering, "Well, what're we waitin' for? I want to see yer old ghost."

"Very well, then," said the four Moffats in solemn voices. "Follow us."

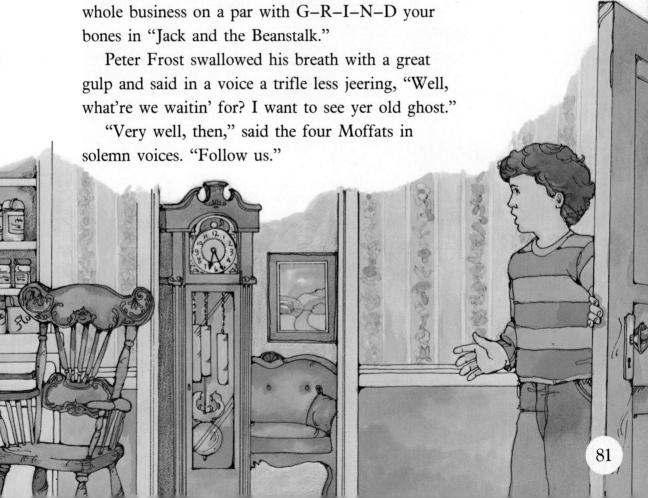

Again they left the warm safety of the kitchen,
mounted the inky black stairs to the second floor,
each one holding to the belt of the one in front.
When they reached the stepladder, they paused a
moment to count heads.

"Aw, you don't think I'm gonna skin out without
seeing your silly old ghost, do yer?" asked Peter
Frost. However, blustering though his words were,
there could be no doubt that his hand, the one that
held onto Joe's belt, was shaking and shaking.

"Now we go up the stepladder," said Joe in a hoarse whisper. "I'll push open the hatch."

Cautiously the five mounted the stepladder. It seemed to lead to a never-ending pit of darkness.

"Why don't you light your flash?" asked Peter Frost, doing his best to sound carefree and easy.

"And scare away the ghost, I suppose," snorted Joe. "You know, a ghost isn't comin' out where there's a light and all this many people. That is, unless there's a certain one around it happens to be interested in."

Another howl interrupted Joe's words. This sounded so close to them now that the four Moffats were afraid Peter Frost would recognize the voice of Catherine-the-cat. But he didn't. He began to shake and shake more violently than ever, making the stepladder they were standing on shiver and creak.

Joe pushed the trap door up with his shoulders. It fell open with a groan just as it had done before. They all climbed in and stood on the attic floor. Except for a pale glow from the light below, the attic was in the thickest blackness. For a moment they stood there in silence. Then suddenly Joe gave a swift flash into the corner of the attic. It fell for a second on the stuffed wildcat.

Peter Frost started but said not a word.

Then swiftly Joe flashed the light in the other corner. The stuffed owl stared at them broodingly.

But Peter Frost said nothing.

And then Joe flashed his light on Madame-the-
ghost, herself. There she was, lurking in the corner,
her orange head gaping horribly. All the children
gasped, but still Peter Frost said nothing. All of a

sudden, without any warning whatsoever, Madame-
the-ghost started careening madly toward them. And
dragging heavy chains behind her too, from the
sound.

Jane called out in a shrill voice:

"Peter Frost! Peter Frost!

E-e-e-e-e-e-e-e-e-e!"

Joe flashed his light on and off rapidly. Madame-
the-ghost dashed wildly round and round the attic.
The same howl rent the air! The shutters banged.
Then Peter Frost let out a roar of terror. That
THING was after HIM. He tore around the attic
room, roaring like a bull. And the ghost, dragging its
horrible chains, tore after him.

"Let me go," he bellowed. But he couldn't find
the hatch. Around the attic and around the attic he
stumbled, kicking over stuffed partridges and quail.
Finally he tripped over the wildcat and sprawled on
the floor. Joe flashed his light on them for a second
and when Peter Frost saw that he was sitting on the
wildcat, he let out another piercing yell and leaped to
his feet. He had seen now where the hatch was and
he meant to escape before that ghost could catch up
with him. Again he tripped and was down once more,
this time with the ghost right on top of him. She
would smother him with those ghastly robes of hers.

"She's got me! She's got me!" he roared.

Frantically he shook himself free of the ghost,
and in wild leaps he made again for the hatch.

But now Rufus and Jane too had stood all they could of this nerve-racking business. They both began howling with fright and screaming, "Mama, Mama!" What with Peter Frost's yelling, Catherine-the-cat's yowling, the screams of Rufus and Jane, Sylvie herself began laughing hysterically and the place sounded like bedlam. To make matters worse, the battery of Joe's flashlight gave out, so there was no way of turning on the light and showing everyone there was no real ghost.

No, the ghost was real enough to Peter Frost, and as he finally reached the hatch and clattered down the stairs he thought he could still feel its cold breath on his neck and cheeks. The four Moffats followed after him, half tumbling, half sliding, until they reached the kitchen. Peter Frost tore out the back door with a bang and left the four of them there in the kitchen, breathless and sobbing and laughing all at once.

Think about the story. Finish the chart on page 75. Then answer the questions.

1. Use your chart. What happens in the attic that the Moffats do not expect? How does it change their plan to scare Peter Frost?

2. Is the setting scarier at the beginning or toward the end of the story? Tell why you think as you do.

3. Peter Frost does not act scared at the beginning of the story. How does Peter change near the end? Why does he change?

4. Jane and Rufus are scared when they are in the attic. Why do they laugh with the others when they come downstairs to the kitchen?

5. This story is in a unit about things that are not what they seem to be. Think about how the story would be different if everything happened as the Moffats planned. Would it still belong in this unit? Give reasons for your answer.

6. Pretend you are the writer. Where would you have set the story to make it scary? Why?

WORK WITH A PARTNER

Tell about a scary place and what makes it scary.
Discuss how scary places are alike and different.
Ask questions about what your classmate says.
Talk about the answers.

Focusing on "The Legend of the Bluebonnet"

Think and Read

▶ Talk about something you own that is very important to you. What makes the possession important? Ask questions about what your classmates say.

▶ Look at the pictures on pages 90–91. Think about what you know about important possessions.

- Which character seems to be holding a very important possession? How can you tell?
- What is the important possession? How might it be important to what happens in the story?

▶ Get ready to read about what happens to the little girl. As you read, think about what the girl does and how she feels as she does it. Think about how you would complete this chart.

What the Girl Does	How She Feels

Now turn the page and read "The Legend of the Bluebonnet." Then you will talk about giving things up for others.

The Legend of the Bluebonnet

**A Comanche legend retold and illustrated
by Tomie dePaola**

"Great Spirits, the land is dying. Your People are dying, too," the long line of dancers sang.

"Tell us what we have done to anger you. End this drought. Save your People. Tell us what we must do so you will send the rain that will bring back life."

For three days, the dancers danced to the sound of the drums, and for three days, the People called Comanche watched and waited. And even though the hard winter was over, no healing rains came.

Drought and famine are hardest on the very young and the very old. Among the few children left was a small girl named She-Who-Is-Alone. She sat by herself watching the dancers. In her lap was a doll made from buckskin—a warrior doll. The eyes, nose and mouth were painted on with the juice of berries. It wore beaded leggings and a belt of polished bone. On its head were brilliant blue feathers from the bird who cries "Jay-jay-jay." She loved her doll very much.

"Soon," She-Who-Is-Alone said to her doll, "the shaman will go off alone to the top of the hill to listen for the words of the Great Spirits. Then, we will know what to do so that once more the rains will come and the Earth will be green and alive. The buffalo will be plentiful and the People will be rich again."

As she talked, she thought of the mother who
made the doll, of the father who brought the blue
feathers. She thought of the grandfather and the
grandmother she had never known. They were all
like shadows. It seemed long ago that they had died
from the famine. The People had named her and
cared for her. The warrior doll was the only thing
she had left from those distant days.

"The sun is setting," the runner called as he ran through the camp. "The shaman is returning."

The People gathered in a circle and the shaman spoke.

"I have heard the words of the Great Spirits," he said. "The People have become selfish. For years, they have taken from the Earth without giving anything back. The Great Spirits say the People must

sacrifice. We must make a burnt offering of the most valued possession among us. The ashes of this offering shall then be scattered to the four points of the Earth, the Home of the Winds. When this sacrifice is made, drought and famine will cease. Life will be restored to the Earth and to the People!"

The People sang a song of thanks to the Great Spirits for telling them what they must do.

"I'm sure it is not my new bow that the Great Spirits want," a warrior said.

"Or my special blanket," a woman added, as everyone went to their tipis to talk and think over what the Great Spirits had asked.

Everyone, that is, except She-Who-Is-Alone. She held her doll tightly to her heart.

"You," she said, looking at the doll. "You are my most valued possession. It is you the Great Spirits want." And she knew what she must do.

As the council fires died out and the tipi flaps began to close, the small girl returned to the tipi, where she slept, to wait.

The night outside was still except for the distant sound of the night bird with the red wings. Soon everyone in the tipi was asleep, except She-Who-Is-Alone. Under the ashes of the tipi fire one stick still glowed. She took it and quietly crept out into the night. She ran to the place on the hill where the Great Spirits had spoken to the shaman. Stars filled the sky, but there was no moon.

"O Great Spirits," She-Who-Is-Alone said, "here is my warrior doll. It is the only thing I have from my family who died in this famine. It is my most valued possession. Please accept it."

Then, gathering twigs, she started a fire with the glowing firestick. The small girl watched as the twigs began to catch and burn. She thought of her grandmother and grandfather, her mother and father and all the People—their suffering, their hunger. And

before she could change her mind, she thrust the doll
into the fire.

She watched until the flames died down and the
ashes had grown cold. Then, scooping up a handful,
She-Who-Is-Alone scattered the ashes to the Home
of the Winds, the North and the East, the South and

the West. And there she fell asleep until the first light of the morning sun woke her.

She looked out over the hill, and stretching out from all sides, where the ashes had fallen, the ground was covered with flowers—beautiful flowers, as blue as the feathers in the hair of the doll, as blue as the feathers of the bird who cries "Jay-jay-jay."

When the People came out of their tipis, they

could scarcely believe their eyes. They gathered on the hill with She-Who-Is-Alone to look at the miraculous sight. There was no doubt about it, the flowers were a sign of forgiveness from the Great Spirits.

And as the People sang and danced their thanks to the Great Spirits, a warm rain began to fall and the land began to live again. From that day on, the

little girl was known by another name—"One-Who-Dearly-Loved-Her-People."

And every spring, the Great Spirits remember the sacrifice of a little girl and fill the hills and valleys of the land, now called Texas, with the beautiful blue flowers.

Even to this very day.

Think about the story. Finish the chart on page 89. Then answer the questions.

1. Use your chart. Also, think about what has happened to the Comanche people. How does She-Who-Is-Alone feel as she watches the dancers? Why do you think she feels this way?

2. Use your chart. How does the girl feel as she gives her doll to the Great Spirits? How do you know?

3. This selection is part of a unit about things that change into something else. Does this selection belong in the unit? Tell why or why not.

4. What does She-Who-Is-Alone receive in return for sacrificing, or giving up, her doll?

5. Why do you think the Great Spirits accept the little girl's sacrifice? Give reasons for your answer.

6. The Great Spirits send blue flowers and rain in return for the doll. Imagine that something else were sacrificed. What might the Great Spirits send instead? Give reasons for your answer.

Talk about reasons that people give up things that are important to them. Discuss how the people might feel. Ask questions about what your classmates say. Talk about the answers.

Focusing on "The Crane Maiden"

▶ Talk about things that you believe bring good luck. Ask questions about what your classmates say.

▶ Look at the picture on page 104. Read the title of the selection. Think about what you know about things that are believed to bring good luck.
  ● What do you think is happening in this picture?
  ● Find something in the picture that might bring good luck to the man. Tell what you think it is.

▶ Get ready to read about what happens to the man. As you read, think about why each event takes place. Think about what you would add to this chart.

Event	What Makes It Happen

Now turn the page and read "The Crane Maiden." Then you will talk about kindness.

The Crane Maiden

A Japanese folk tale retold by Miyoko Matsutani

English version by Alvin Tresselt

Illustrated by Masami Miyamoto

Long years ago, at the edge of a small mountain village in the snow country of Japan, there lived an old man and his wife. They had little in this world that they could call their own. But they were happy in their life together.

Now one winter morning the old man set out for the village with a bundle of firewood fastened to his back. It was bitter cold. He knew he would have little trouble selling the wood. Then with the money, he would buy some food so that he and his wife could have a good supper.

As the old man trudged through the falling snow, he was suddenly aware of a fluttering sound, and a pitiful cry of *Koh, koh*. Turning from the path to investigate, he came upon a great crane frantically trying to free herself from a trap.

The old man's heart was touched with pity for the magnificent bird. While he tried to soothe the crane with tender words, his hands released the cruel spring of the trap. At once the crane flew up, joyfully calling *Koh, koh,* and disappeared into the snowy sky.

With a lighter step the old man went on through the snow. And when he had sold his wood, he returned once more to his humble house. While his old wife busied herself with preparing supper, he told her about rescuing the crane.

"That was a good deed," she said. "Surely the gods will one day reward you for your kind heart."

As she spoke these words, there came a tapping on the door. The old wife hurried to see who was there. Upon opening the door, she saw a beautiful young girl standing in the swirling snow. Her delicate face glowed like a peach beginning to ripen in the summer sun. And her dark eyes sparkled in the dancing firelight.

"Forgive my knocking at your door," she said in a soft voice, "but I have lost my way in the snow. May I share the warmth of your fire tonight?" Then bowing low before the two old people, she said, "My name is Tsuru (SOO•roo)."

"Oh, you poor child!" cried the old wife. "Come in at once before you freeze in the bitter cold." They sat the girl down close to the hearth. Then the old wife piled more wood on the flames so that the girl would soon be warm.

The old couple shared their simple supper of hot porridge with Tsuru-san, all the time feasting their eyes on her great beauty. Then they gave her their bed with its warm quilts to sleep on, while they spent the night huddled on a pile of straw.

In the morning when they awoke, the old man and his wife were surprised to see a good fire already burning on the hearth. The water jar was filled with fresh clear water, the floors had been swept, and all the rooms were clean and tidy.

Tsuru-san, the sleeves of her kimono neatly tied back with a red cord, was busily stirring a pot over the fire. "Good morning," she said, bowing to the old couple. "If you will wash your hands we may eat breakfast, for the porridge is cooked and ready."

"In our old age we have a daughter!" said the old man, laughing.

"It is the gods smiling on us for your good deed of yesterday," replied his wife happily.

The snow and bitter cold continued for many days. And so Tsuru-san stayed in the shelter of the old couple's home. As she had neither mother nor father, it was at last decided that she would remain as a daughter to these people.

The children of the neighborhood were soon attracted to the house as Tsuru-san was such a delight to be with. The house rang with happy laughter. The hearts of the old man and his wife were filled with joy at the sound.

And so the days of early winter passed. Soon it was time for the great New Year celebration. The old man spoke to his wife, saying, "Tsuru-san has been such a delight to us. If only I could give her a gift of a new kimono."

"Or if I could make her a rice cake for the New Year," his wife added.

But, alas, the winter had been hard. The old man had not been able to cut wood to sell. There was no money to buy even rice, much less a kimono.

Now Tsuru-san had heard them talking. It saddened her that these good people should be so poor. Coming before them she bowed low and said, "Dear parents, I know there has been no wood to sell. But perhaps I can help you and repay your great kindness to me. There is an old loom in the back room. I will weave cloth on it for you to sell in the village. Only you must promise that no one shall look at me while I am weaving."

The old man and his wife thought this was an odd request, but they quickly agreed. Tsuru-san locked herself in the room. Soon the old man and

his wife heard the sound of

> *Tin kola, kola, pon, pon,*
>
> *Tin kola, kola, pon, pon*

as the shuttle sped back and forth and the fabric grew in length.

For three days this continued. Tsuru-san stopped for neither food nor rest. Then at last the door opened and she stepped out, holding in her hands a bolt of cloth such as the old man and his wife had never seen in all their lives. They gasped at its beauty and marveled at its softness.

"Dear father," said the girl, "take this cloth into the village and sell it. It will be but small payment for the happy home you have given me."

Without wasting a moment, the old man hurried into the center of the village. When people saw the beautiful cloth he was carrying, a crowd soon gathered.

"I will pay ten gold pieces for your cloth," said one man.

"No, no!" cried another. "Sell it to me for twenty gold pieces!"

Each person who saw the cloth offered more money than the one before, until the old man finally sold the cloth for one hundred pieces of gold.

Stopping only long enough to buy rice for rice cakes, a kimono for Tsuru-san, and a few treats for New Year's Day, the man hurried home with his pockets jingling. "Tomorrow, tomorrow is the New Year's Day," he sang. "The New Year is the happy time, eating rice cakes whiter than snow."

Then such a hustle and bustle there was, as the old man and his wife prepared for the feast. As the old man pounded the rice, his wife made it into fine white cakes. And on New Year's Day all the children came in for a great party with their friend Tsuru-san.

Still the cold days of winter followed one after the other. At last one day Tsuru-san said to the old couple, "It is time for me to weave another bolt of cloth for you so that you will have money to live until the spring returns. But remember what I told you. No one is to look at me while I am working."

Again they promised. And the girl once more locked herself in the room and began weaving.

Tin kola, kola, pon, pon,
Tin kola, pon, pon

went the loom.

One day passed, and then the second. Still the sound of the loom filled the house. By now, the neighbors had grown curious.

"Is Tsuru-san weaving again?" asked one.

"Ah, soon you will have more gold pieces to hide under the floor," said another with a smile and a wink.

"The loom makes such an interesting sound," remarked the first one. "I would love to see what Tsuru-san is doing."

"We have promised not to watch her while she works," said the old man.

"What an odd request," cried one of the people. "I would not make such a promise to *my* daughter, you can believe me. What harm could there be in taking one look?"

Now in truth, the old woman had been most curious about Tsuru-san's weaving. Encouraged by her neighbor's remarks, she stepped up to a crack in the door.

"Stop, stop, old woman!" cried her husband when he saw what was happening. But it was too late. His wife had already peeked through the crack.

What a sight it was that met her eye! There, sitting at the loom, was a great white crane, pulling feathers from her body and weaving them into cloth.

The old woman stepped back. Before she could tell what she had seen, the door opened. Out stepped Tsuru-san, thin and pale, holding in her hands a half-finished bolt of cloth.

"Dear parents," she said in a weak voice, "I am the crane you rescued from the trap. I wanted to repay your kindness by weaving you another bolt of cloth." Then her eyes filled with tears. "But now that you have seen me in my true form I can no longer stay with you."

With this she kissed the man and his wife tenderly, and walked out of the house. Instantly she became a crane once more and, with a great whish of her wings, flew up into the sky. Slowly she circled overhead. Then with a single cry of *Koh* as if to say good-bye, the crane maiden was gone forever.

Think about the story. Finish the chart on page 103. Then answer the questions.

1. Use your chart. Think about how the old man planned to spend his morning. How does helping the crane change what happens to him?

2. Use your chart. Think about Tsuru's stay with the old man and woman. What reason does she give for staying longer? What is her real reason?

3. Why must no one see Tsuru while she is weaving? Explain Tsuru's secret.

4. The selections in this unit are about things that are not what they seem to be. What is not what it seems to be in this story?

5. What do the neighbors say to make the old woman break her promise to Tsuru?

6. What might have happened if the old woman had not peeked into the room where Tsuru was weaving?

WORK IN A GROUP

Talk about kindness. Talk about whether or not it is important to repay an act of kindness. Ask questions about what your classmates say. Talk about the answers.

Focusing on "Animals as Symbols"

▶ Talk about an animal you know about. Tell what that animal is like. Ask questions about what your classmates say.

▶ Read the title and look at the pictures on pages 118–119. Think about what you know about animals.
- What do you think the title means?
- How might each of the birds be a symbol?

▶ Get ready to read about how people used animals as symbols. As you read, think about how each group of people chose and used its symbol. Copy this diagram. Fill it in as you read.

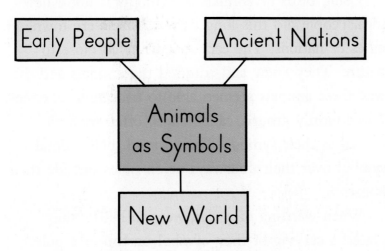

Now turn the page and read "Animals as Symbols."
Then you will talk about an animal symbol.

Animals as Symbols

To the Japanese, the crane is special. Artists paint it. Poets write poems about it. Many people honor it in their folk tales. The crane is a *symbol* (SIM·buhl), or something that stands for something else. In Japan, the crane stands for good fortune or good luck. The crane brought luck to the old people in the Japanese tale "The Crane Maiden."

Symbols of Early Peoples

Using birds or animals as symbols is not a new idea. People did this long before there were towns or cities or nations. The early people lived close to nature. They knew and admired the animals and the way these animals seemed able to trick their enemies. Large family groups, called *clans*, often took an animal as their symbol. They carved their animal symbol over their doorways or on poles outside their houses.

When warriors of a clan went to battle, they placed a carving of their symbol on top of a pole. If the warriors got separated during a battle, they looked for their symbol and were able to find their leader.

Illustrated by Robert Masheris

Symbols of Ancient Nations

More than 5,000 years ago, soldiers in ancient
Egypt used the falcon as their symbol. The falcon
stood for the Egyptian king, or *pharaoh* (FAIR·oh).
The people believed that the pharaoh really was a
falcon in a human form.

In ancient Greece, cities had symbols. Soldiers
from the city of Athens used an owl as their symbol.
Soldiers from the city of Corinth fought under the
symbol of a winged horse. The Roman army used
the eagle as its symbol.

Symbols in the New World

Long before Europeans came to America, the American Indians were organized into clans, tribes, and even nations. The Iroquois Indians had eight clans. Each had an animal or bird as its symbol. The clans took the names of their symbols: Wolf, Deer, Bear, Beaver, Turtle, Snipe (a bird of the marshes), Heron, and Hawk. The clan's symbol was carved or painted above the doorway of every Iroquois house.

Members of the same clan thought of themselves as brothers and sisters. If a man of a Wolf clan visited a distant Iroquois village, he would go at once to a house with a wolf over the door. There he was sure to be welcomed as a brother, even though he was a total stranger.

About a thousand years ago, Vikings landed in North America. It is possible that the first true flag to fly over America had a raven on it. (A raven is like a crow, but larger.) The raven was a symbol of the Vikings. Their symbol was known as "Raven, Terror of the Land."

In the 1700s, when America was being settled, many symbols were suggested for the new nation: a bucking horse, a beaver, a codfish, a deer, a wild turkey, and a pine tree. At that time, the symbol most widely used in America was the rattlesnake. In 1776, at the time of the American Revolution, rattlesnake flags were flown over many battlefields where Americans were fighting for independence from England. The words on the flag were a warning to England. (The word *tread* means "step.")

The American bald eagle was finally chosen as the symbol of America. On July 4, 1776, the day the Declaration of Independence was signed, Congress appointed three men to design a national seal, or symbol. Those men were Benjamin Franklin, John Adams, and Thomas Jefferson. It took them years to decide on what would be the best symbol for their new nation. Others joined with them to help. Benjamin Franklin was in France in 1782, when the final decision was made: the American bald eagle would be the national bird and symbol. Franklin was disappointed. He had wanted the wild turkey to be our national bird.

Here is the seal of the United States of America. At its center is the dignified and powerful American eagle. When Americans see this eagle, they know that it stands for, or *symbolizes*, America and its people.

Think and Discuss

Think about the selection. Look at the diagram you completed as you read. Then answer the questions.

1. Use your diagram. Which group of people believed that their leader really was the animal they used as a group symbol?

2. Use your diagram. How did having a carved symbol on top of a pole help people of the early clans?

3. Look at the picture on page 121. Why do you think the Vikings wanted an animal that would stand for the "Terror of the Land"?

4. The selections in this unit are about things that change from one form to another. How does this selection fit into the unit?

5. What does having the bald eagle as a symbol say about Americans as a group? Explain your answer.

6. Think about other symbols suggested for the United States. What symbol would you choose? How would it change the way people see America?

WORK IN A GROUP

Talk about symbols. Can you think of symbols for schools, clubs, sports teams, and businesses? Make a list of different groups' symbols. Tell what they show about the groups. Discuss your list with classmates.

Think and Read

▶ Think about Halloween. Talk about animals and other things that are symbols of Halloween. Ask questions about what your classmates say.

▶ Look at the pictures on pages 126–127 and 129. Think about what you know about Halloween.

- What symbols of Halloween do you see in the pictures?
- How might the poems be alike and be different?

▶ Get ready to read the two poems. As you read, think about the sounds, things, and actions in the poems that make them spooky. Think about what you would add to these diagrams.

sounds   things   sounds   things

"What Night Would It Be?"   "What the Gray Cat Sings"

actions   actions

Now turn the page and read the poems. Then you will talk about spooky things.

What Night Would It Be?

A poem by John Ciardi

If the moon shines
On the black pines
And an owl flies
And a ghost cries
And the hairs rise
On the back
  on the back
    on the back of your neck—

If you look quick
At the moon-slick
On the black air
And what goes there
Rides a broom-stick
And if things pick
At the back
  at the back
    at the back of your neck—

Would you know then
By the small men
With the lit grins
And with no chins,
By the owl's *hoo*,
And the ghost's *boo*,
By the Tom Cat,
And the Black Bat,
On the night air,
And the thing there,
By the thing,
  by the thing,
    by the dark thing there

(Yes, you do,
  yes, you do
    know the thing I mean)

That it's now,
  that it's now,
    that it's—Halloween!

Illustrated by Sharron O'Neil

127

What the Gray Cat Sings

A poem by Arthur Guiterman

The Cat was once a weaver,
   A weaver, a weaver,
An old and withered weaver
   Who labored late and long;
And while she made the shuttle hum
And wove the weft and clipped the thrum,
Beside the loom with droning drum
   She sang the weaving song:
     "Pr-rrum, pr-rrum,
Thr-ree thr-reads in the thr-rum,
     Pr-rrum!"

The Cat's no more a weaver,
   A weaver, a weaver,
An old and wrinkled weaver,
   For though she did no wrong,
A witch hath changed the shape of her
That dwindled down and clothed in fur
Beside the hearth with droning purr
   She thrums her weaving song:
     "Pr-rrum, pr-rrum,
Thr-ree thr-reads in the thr-rum,
     Pr-rrum!"

Illustrated by Marie-Louise Gay

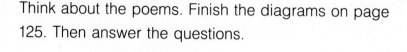

Think about the poems. Finish the diagrams on page 125. Then answer the questions.

1. Use your diagram. Think about "What Night Would It Be?" How does the writer make you feel the spookiness of the night?

2. Read the words that are repeated at the end of each verse in "What Night Would It Be?" How would the poem change if they were said only once? Give reasons for your answer.

3. Use your diagram. Think about "What the Gray Cat Sings." How does the writer make you feel the spookiness of the night?

4. Think about "What the Gray Cat Sings." Read the words that are repeated. How would the poem change if these words were said only once? Give reasons for your answer.

5. These poems belong to a unit about things that are not what they seem. What things in the poems are not what they seem?

6. Compare the poems. Which poem is spookier? Give reasons for your answer. What would you add to the other to make it spookier?

Talk about spooky things. Are they the same as scary things? Why or why not? Ask questions about what your classmates say. Talk about the answers.

WORK IN A GROUP

In the picture, each person is giving the answer *fiction.* That's because all three stories are made up. All such imaginary stories are fiction. Now if you asked what *kind* of fiction each person is reading, you would get three different answers. The first person would say *realistic fiction.* The second person would say *a folk tale.* The third person would answer *a fantasy.* Each story is an example of a different kind of fiction.

Although there are many kinds of fiction, the following chart tells you about these three.

Three Kinds of Fiction

Realistic Fiction

The story usually takes place in the present.
The story is imaginary but could probably happen.
The main characters may remind you of people
you know.
The story has an author.

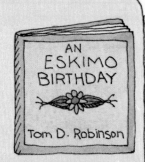

Folk Tale

Ordinary people often have their wishes granted.
Most of the characters act only one way—always
good, always bad, silly, clever.
Some magic may happen—witches may cast spells
or people may receive magic objects.
People made up the folk tale long ago.
The words *retold by* and the storyteller's name
may appear with the tale.

Fantasy

Magical things happen—people fly or animals and
toys talk.
The story has an author.

Here are six fiction books you might find in the library. Read the title and the description of each story. On a sheet of paper, write *realistic fiction, folk tale,* or *fantasy* to tell what kind of fiction is in each book.

1 "Did You Carry the Flag Today, Charlie?" REBECCA CAUDILL

Charlie is having a terrible time in first grade. He is very curious and is always getting into trouble. He never seems to behave well enough to have the honor of carrying the flag.

2 THE FOOL OF THE WORLD AND THE FLYING SHIP RETOLD BY Arthur Ransome

A poor young man, called the Fool of the World, finds a flying ship and meets seven people with magic powers. When the Fool must perform several difficult tasks to please the Czar, his new friends help him.

3 The Amazing Bone William Steig

Pearl, a pig, meets a talking bone. They like each other immediately and start home together. On the way, a fox catches Pearl for his dinner, and the talking bone must try to save her.

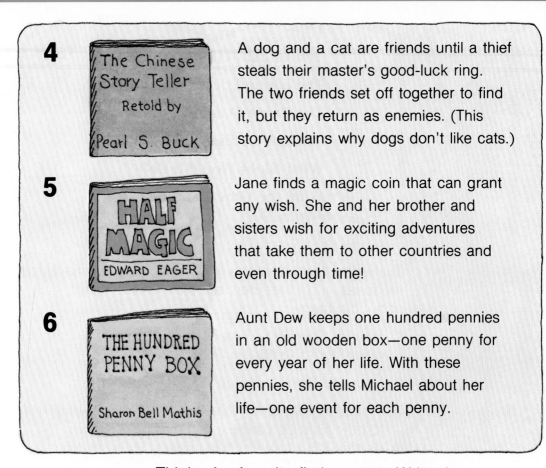

4 The Chinese Story Teller Retold by Pearl S. Buck

A dog and a cat are friends until a thief steals their master's good-luck ring. The two friends set off together to find it, but they return as enemies. (This story explains why dogs don't like cats.)

5 HALF MAGIC EDWARD EAGER

Jane finds a magic coin that can grant any wish. She and her brother and sisters wish for exciting adventures that take them to other countries and even through time!

6 THE HUNDRED PENNY BOX Sharon Bell Mathis

Aunt Dew keeps one hundred pennies in an old wooden box—one penny for every year of her life. With these pennies, she tells Michael about her life—one event for each penny.

Think of a favorite fiction story. Write the story's title, the author's name, and what *kind* of fiction it is. Be prepared to tell your classmates why you think your story is realistic fiction, a folk tale, or a fantasy.

You have read these selections.

The Ghost in the Attic

The Legend of the Bluebonnet

The Crane Maiden

Animals as Symbols

What Night Would It Be?

What the Gray Cat Sings

Talk about the selections you have read. Consider how the ideas and characters are alike and different. Talk about the theme.

1. How is "The Ghost in the Attic" different from the other stories in this unit?

2. How are Tsuru and She-Who-Is-Alone alike?

3. Which selections explain how something came to be? What do they explain and how do they explain it?

4. The stories and poems are about people or things that changed. Which change did you most enjoy reading about? Tell why you think as you do.

BOOKSHELF

The Enchanted Caribou by Elizabeth Cleaver. Atheneum, 1986. In this Inuit tale, three young hunters become friends with a young woman who is turned into a white caribou.

The Ghost on Saturday Night by Sid Fleischman. Little, Brown, 1974. Opie guides a mean-looking stranger through the thick fog. His reward is two tickets to a ghost raising. Opie doesn't know he has front-row seats to a bank robbery, too.

The Heavenly Zoo retold by Alison Lurie. Farrar, Straus & Giroux, 1979. A collection of tales from all over the world to explain the shapes people see in the star groups called the *constellations*.

A-Haunting We Will Go: Ghostly Stories and Poems collected by Lee Bennett Hopkins. Albert Whitman, 1977. Some of these ghost stories and poems will make you laugh. Some will make you shiver.

The Shrinking of Treehorn by Florence Parry Heide. Holiday House, 1971. Treehorn sees that shelves are getting higher and his clothes are getting looser. Can he really be shrinking?

3 Across the Land and Sea

TALKING ABOUT THE THEME

Look at the picture on pages 138 and 139 and read the title.

1. What is happening in the picture?

2. The book in the picture is being used as a magic carpet. What does this tell you?

3. What faraway places have you visited as you read the first two units of this book?

4. What are the most interesting places you have visited through books? What books took you there?

5. How do you think the selections in this unit will be alike?

Other Books About Journeys

Journey Home by Yoshiko Uchida. Atheneum, 1978. A Japanese-American family tries to return to their old life in California after being held in a Utah camp during the first years of World War II.

Maria Luisa by Winifred Madison. Lippincott, 1971. When Maria moves from Arizona to California, she finds herself in a new world with new problems to face.

Journey to America by Sonia Levitin. Atheneum, 1970. A family flees from the Nazis. They are helped by many strangers as they try to make their way to America.

140

Focusing on "Building the Erie Canal" and "The Erie Canal"

▶ On a sheet of paper, quickly write as much as you can about transportation. After you have finished, share your ideas with others.

▶ Read the titles and look at the pictures on pages 142–147. Think about what you know about transportation.

- What kind of transportation will you read about?
- Which selection do you think will give facts?

▶ As you read, look for facts about the Erie Canal. Think about what you would add to this chart.

Building the Erie Canal	
Who	
When	
Where	
Why	
How	

Now turn the page and read the selections. Then you will discuss how hard work helps to build America.

Think and Read

Building the Erie Canal

An article

In the 1800's Americans were trying to solve the problems of transportation to the west. One solution was to build a long canal across New York State to Lake Erie.

The Erie Canal was begun in 1817. Thousands of immigrants, using shovels and pickaxes, had to dig the canal through a wilderness of swamps and forests.

Completed in 1825, the Erie Canal was 4 feet deep and 363 miles long. Horses, mules, and oxen were used to pull the boats and rafts that carried people, food, goods, and animals back and forth. A fast speed was eighty miles in twenty-four hours. Whenever a low bridge was approached, the cry went out, "Low bridge, everybody down!"

After eight years of work, the Erie Canal finally provided a route through the Appalachian Mountains and opened up the way west.

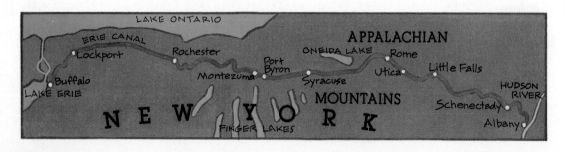

Illustrated by Dennis Ziemienski

The Erie Canal

A folk song

Illustrated by Peter Spier

1. I've got a mule, her name is Sal, Fif-teen miles on the
2. We better get on our way, old gal, Fif-teen miles on the

E-rie Ca-nal. She's a good old work-er and a good old pal,
E-rie Ca-nal. 'Cause you bet your life I'd nev-er part with Sal,

Fif-teen miles on the E-rie Ca-nal. We've hauled some barg-es in our day,
Fif-teen miles on the E-rie Ca-nal. Git up there, mule, here comes a lock,

Filled with lum-ber, coal, and hay, And we know ev-'ry
We'll make Rome 'bout six o'-clock, Just one more trip and

inch of the way From Al-ba-ny to Buf-fa-lo.
back we'll go Right back home to Buf-fa-lo.

Refrain

Low bridge, ev-'ry-bod-y down! Low bridge, for we're go-ing through a town, And you'll

al-ways know your neigh-bor, You'll al-ways know your pal, If you

ev-er nav-i-gat-ed on the E-rie Ca-nal.

I've got a mule, her name is Sal,
Fifteen miles on the Erie Canal.
She's a good old worker and a good old pal,
Fifteen miles on the Erie Canal.

We've hauled some barges in our day,
Filled with lumber, coal, and hay,
And we know ev'ry inch of the way
From Albany to Buffalo.

Low bridge, ev'rybody down!
Low bridge, for we're going through a town,

And you'll always know your neighbor,
You'll always know your pal,
If you ever navigated on the Erie Canal.

Think and Discuss

Think about the selections. Finish the chart on page 141. Then answer the questions.

1. Use your chart. How many years did it take to complete the Erie Canal? Why do you think it took so long to complete?

2. Use your chart. What problem was solved by the canal?

3. Why would you suppose people used to sing the song "The Erie Canal"?

4. Who do you think worked harder, the people who built the canal or the people who worked on the boats and barges? Tell why you think as you do.

5. If you were a canal worker, what job would you want? Why?

6. These selections are part of a unit about journeys to new lands. In what way did the hard work of the canal builders help people journey to new lands?

WORK IN A GROUP

Talk about how working hard helps our country. Discuss what makes people work hard. Ask questions about what your classmates say. Talk about the answers.

Focusing on "Half a Kingdom"

▶ Talk about a time you were lost. Ask questions about what your classmates say.

▶ Look at the picture on pages 150–151. Read the title and the first page of the story. Think about what you know about being lost.
   • What is happening in the picture?
   • Who do you think will find the lost prince?

▶ Prince Lini and Signy are two of the characters you will meet in this folk tale. As you read, look for details that tell how they act and what they do. Think about what you might add to these diagrams.

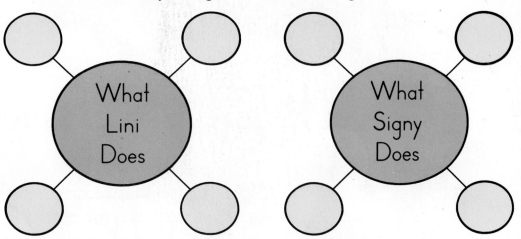

Now turn the page and read "Half a Kingdom." Then you will talk about how leaders rule their countries.

Half a Kingdom

An Icelandic folk tale retold by Ann McGovern
Illustrated by Jane Teiko Oka

When you wake up in the morning, you never can tell what might happen to you during the day.

One fine morning, Prince Lini woke up in his castle on the hill. He didn't have the slightest idea what was going to happen to him that day.

He rode into the forest with his friends. Suddenly, from nowhere, a thick cold fog blew into the woods. The cloud of fog covered the prince from head to toe. A minute later the fog drifted away and was gone. Gone, too, was Prince Lini.

His friends searched for him all that day and all that night. And in the morning they rode to the castle to tell the king the strange story of the fog that rolled in from the sky and took away his son.

Now the king loved his son more than anything, even more than the riches of his kingdom,
which he loved very much. He sent for his
strongest men and his wisest men. "Whoever
finds Prince Lini," he said, "and brings him back
to me, will win half of my kingdom."

The strongest men (and those not so strong)
searched far and wide. The wisest men (and
those not so wise) searched wide and far. All
over the kingdom people heard the news that the
prince had disappeared in a cloud of fog. Anyone
who had ever wanted half a kingdom set out to
search for the prince.

One fine morning, Signy, a poor peasant girl, woke up in her cottage at the edge of the forest. She didn't have the slightest idea what was going to happen to her that day.

But she had heard about the missing prince and about the king's reward of half the kingdom. She knew that the strongest and the wisest men had looked far and wide.

I'll look near and narrow, she thought.

Signy knew the secret places of the forest better than anyone else. She put on a pair of sturdy shoes for walking and took along some food. And she set out to search for Prince Lini.

All that day she looked. She saw nothing but tree shapes in the snow. All that day she called. She heard nothing but the song of the icy wind.

The sun began to set and the sky turned rosy. Soon it would be dark. Signy walked through a narrow place between the rocks to her favorite warm cave and peered inside. There, stretched out on a golden bed, was Prince Lini, fast asleep.

She ran into the cave and tried to wake him. But he slept on, in a deep, deep sleep.

All of a sudden she heard a clattering, a chattering. She ran to hide in the darkest corner of the cave.

Two troll girls—a tall troll and a shorter troll—entered the cave. "Fee, Foo, Fum, Firl. I smell the flesh of a human girl," sang the short troll.

"No," said the tall troll, "it's only Prince Lini."

Then the trolls whistled. Signy listened carefully to the notes of the whistle. Two swans flew into the cave. The short troll said:

Sing O sing O swans of mine,
Sing Prince Lini awake.

The swans sang. Prince Lini stirred, rubbed his eyes, and sat up.

"Now," said the short troll, "for the ninety-seventh time, will you marry one of us?"

"Never," said the prince. "Never, never, never."

"You'll be sorry," the tall troll said. Then she commanded the swans:

Sing O sing O swans of mine,
Sing Prince Lini asleep.

The swans sang and Prince Lini fell fast asleep again. The swans flew out of the cave.

From her hiding place, Signy could see and hear everything. The next morning the trolls left the cave with a clattering and a chattering. Signy crept from her hiding place. She remembered how the trolls whistled, and she whistled the same notes.

The swans flew into the cave. Signy said:

Sing O sing O swans of mine,
Sing Prince Lini awake.

The swans sang.

Prince Lini stirred, rubbed his eyes, sat up, and rubbed his eyes again. "Troll!" he said. "What has happened to you? You look very different."

"I'm not a troll," said Signy, "and nothing has happened to me except that I found you. I'm Signy."

"I'm very pleased to meet you," said the prince.

The prince told Signy how the trolls had cast a spell upon him with their magic fog and how they were holding him a prisoner until he agreed to marry one of them.

Then Signy told the prince how sad the king was, and how he had even offered half the kingdom to anyone who found his son and brought him home.

"No one has found me yet except you," said the prince. "But I don't know whether I *want* to be found. It's nice and warm in this cave. It's nice to have the trolls asking me to marry them every day."

Signy gave the prince a funny look.

"That wasn't true," said the prince. "The real reason is that I don't want to go home. It makes me sad to see how the kingdom is run. And the king will listen to no one. The rich are too rich and hardly work. The poor are too poor and work too hard."

"Yes," said Signy sadly.

The prince looked at Signy and began to laugh. He jumped up and down on the golden bed, laughing and laughing.

"What's so funny about being poor?" Signy asked.

"That's just it!" cried the prince. "You won't be poor if you get half the kingdom and you can share it with everyone! Please, Signy, take me back to the king and take half the kingdom. Please!"

"First things first," said Signy. "The first thing is to get you out of here."

"Why can't we run away right now while I'm awake?" said the prince.

"No," said Signy. "The trolls would surely send down their magic fog before we got out of the woods. They would make me a prisoner, too, along with you. You must find out from the trolls where they go and what they do during the day. It's the only way."

The prince agreed.

The sun began to set and the sky turned rosy. Then Signy whistled. The swans flew into the cave and sang Prince Lini asleep.

Again Signy hid in the dark corner. Soon the trolls came in with a clattering, a chattering. They woke Prince Lini in their usual way. And in their usual way they asked him their usual question.

"Now," said the tall troll, "for the ninety-eighth time, will you marry one of us?"

The prince pretended to think about it. "Tell me," he said, "where do you go and what do you do during the day?"

"We go to the big oak tree in the middle of the forest," the tall troll said.

"And we take out our giant golden egg," the short troll said.

"And we toss it back and forth, and back and forth," the tall troll said.

"What happens if you drop it?" Prince Lini asked.

"Oh, we never drop it," the short troll said. "If we drop it and it breaks, we would disappear forever."

"Enough of this chatter," said the tall troll. "Now for the ninety-ninth time, will you marry one of us?"

"Never, never, never, never, NEVER!" said the prince.

"Oh," said the tall troll, shaking with rage. "Tomorrow you will see how sorry you will be!"

"The end is near for you," said the short troll.

The trolls whistled. The swans sang and Prince Lini slept.

The next morning when the trolls left the cave, Signy whistled for the swans. The swans sang and Prince Lini awoke.

"You were wonderful," Signy said. "Now we will go to the middle of the forest to the big oak tree. You must do exactly what I tell you." And she whispered her plan to the prince.

They left the cave and walked to the middle of the forest. There they saw the two trolls under the big oak tree. The trolls were throwing the giant golden egg to and fro, to and fro.

Signy whispered to the prince, "Be careful. Your life is in danger."

Prince Lini picked up a stone. He aimed carefully and threw it. The stone hit the giant golden egg. It fell to the ground, broken to bits.

Suddenly from nowhere a thick cold fog blew into the woods. The cloud of fog covered the two trolls. A minute later the fog drifted away and was gone. And gone, too, were the trolls. Gone forever, to the place where trolls live.

Signy and Prince Lini ran all the way to the palace. "Wait outside," Signy told the prince. "It's better if I see your father alone."

"Who are you?" the king asked when he saw Signy. "And what do you want?"

"I am Signy, a peasant girl," she said, "and I want half of your kingdom, for I found your son."

"Don't be silly," said the king. "How can a girl find my son when my strongest and my wisest men could not find him!"

"That's too bad for them," Signy said. "If what I say is true, will you keep your promise and give me half of your kingdom?"

"Go away," said the king. "It can't be true."

Signy ran to the door and flung it open. The king was beside himself with joy to see his lost

son. After the two hugged and cried tears of
happiness, Prince Lini told his father about the
trolls and the magic spell and how Signy found
him and freed him.

"Now will you give up half your kingdom?"
Signy asked the king.

"Oh, my precious kingdom!" the king sighed.

"What about your precious son and your
promise!" said the prince.

The king looked at Signy carefully. "A girl
like you found my son? A peasant girl—not even
a princess! But my precious son is right. And a
promise is a promise. I give you half my kingdom."

Prince Lini turned to Signy. "I love you," he said. "Will you marry me? I'll help you rule your half of the kingdom, if you like."

Signy said, "Let's play checkers while I think it over."

They played checkers and Signy thought it over. She thought it would be wonderful to marry Prince Lini. "We can share half the kingdom and share adventures, too, for the rest of our lives," she told him.

And that is exactly what they did, happily and forever after.

Think about the story. Finish the diagrams on page 149. Then answer the questions.

1. What reward does the king offer for the return of his son? Is it a fair reward? Tell why you think as you do.

2. Why is Prince Lini unhappy about the way his father rules the kingdom? What does this tell the reader about Lini?

3. At first the king does not want to keep his promise because Signy is very poor. Does being poor make someone a bad leader? Tell why you think as you do.

4. Why is this selection part of a unit about journeys to new places? Look at the table of contents of your book. In which other unit(s) might this story belong?

5. Use your diagrams. Think about what Lini does in this story. Will Lini make a good leader? Tell why or why not.

6. Use your diagrams. Think about what Signy does in this story. Will Signy make a good leader? Tell why or why not.

**WORK IN
A GROUP**

Lini says that the king will listen to no one. Why is listening important for leaders? What happens when leaders do not listen? Ask questions about what your classmates say.

Focusing on "Steal Away Home"

▶ On a sheet of paper, quickly write as much as you can about how someone you know overcame a problem. Share your ideas with your classmates.

▶ Look at the pictures on pages 168 and 169. Think about what you know about overcoming problems.
  • When and where might this story take place?
  • What problems must the two boys overcome?

▶ Get ready to read about a dangerous trip. As you read, look for problems and how the characters solve them. Think about what you might add to this drawing.

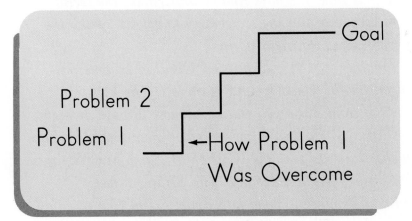

Goal

Problem 2

Problem 1 ← How Problem 1 Was Overcome

Now turn the page and read "Steal Away Home." Then you will talk about what you have to do to reach a goal.

From
Steal Away Home

A novel by Jean Kristof
Illustrated by Phill Renaud

What a powerful—and secret—word freedom *was to the slaves. Many slaves risked their lives trying to reach the North to be free. Amos and Obediah knew that their father had made the dangerous journey and was free. He lived up North in the big city of Philadelphia.*

Amos and Obediah still lived with their mother and sister on a plantation in Searsville, South Carolina. One hot summer day, a minister stopped by their slave shack and spent time talking to the boys' mother. Soon after that talk, the boys finally understood the secret word freedom *and the secret way to get it: "Take the Underground Railroad north."*

On July 4, 1853, Amos and Obediah became passengers on the Underground Railroad. The boys ran barefoot from station to station, almost always at night and always afraid of being caught. Their second station on the Railroad was the home of Mr. and Mrs. Strauss in Raleigh, North Carolina. The Strausses were German immigrants who had come to America to enjoy its freedom. They wanted to share that freedom with all the slaves they could.

This is Amos's account of how the Strauss family helped him and his brother Obie on their way to being free.

Mr. and Mrs. Strauss looked very much alike. They were both small, frail-looking and gray-haired, but they didn't seem old or tired. It's hard to really explain, but their wrinkled faces seemed kind of transparent. In some funny way they made me think of the beat-up hurricane lamp in the Brickers' barn; you hardly noticed the chips and cracks in its chimney when you saw the bright flame inside.

They lived in two small rooms over the pharmacy with little furniture but a lot of books. We had never been in a white person's house before, except once in a while in the Brickers' kitchen, and at first we felt mighty strange and uncomfortable. The Strausses must have understood our feeling, because they did everything they could to make us welcome. Whenever they could get away from their customers one or the other would come up the stairs to us, bringing something nice to eat or some game or trick to entertain us. They even let me look at one of the books with very fancy, exciting pictures in it. I knew they were being kind, but I just kept wishing they would go back to the store and leave us to ourselves.

In the evening when the store was closed Mr. Strauss unfolded a big sheet of paper all covered with lines and markings, and began to pore over it, muttering names like "Searsville," "Richmond," "Washington," and "Philadelphia."

Obie, always curious, asked, "What's that, Master Strauss?"

"That, my boy, is a map. That is a picture of where you have been and where you must go."

Obie and I crowded around him.

"Raleigh is here and there is Philadelphia. There you must go."

"But that isn't very far at all, Master Strauss. We can do that real quick," exclaimed Obie. "Where did we come from?"

"Hm, let me see. This village Searsville, it is here. Just over the line in South Carolina."

Obie's face fell. "But we been gone more than a week. We got to be farther than that."

Mr. Strauss chuckled. "Everything is small on the map. You have come about a hundred miles, more or less. You must go still—let me see—two hundred sixty to Washington, to Philadelphia must be about four hundred miles."

That sounded like a long, long way.

"But now," continued Mr. Strauss, "we shall plot only the next step. We must get you here, to Dr. Culpepper in Henderson. Do you know your letters, my boys?"

"I know *B*," said Obie proudly. "That's the first letter in Bricker and it's on the sign on his driveway. Amos knows more than me, though. Pa started to teach him before they took him away."

"He just taught me a few, and I forgot them pretty well," I admitted.

"That is a great trouble. How to find the way when you cannot read the sign and you cannot ask the people. Well, we must think."

He scratched his head, wrinkled up his forehead and talked for a while to his wife in a foreign language. Then he turned to us and switched back to English.

"We have the plot," he announced. "You must go by day. At night you shall be lost. You were sent to Raleigh by Dr. Culpepper to try if any pharmacy has a certain new medicine. You found it at my store and now you take it back to him. You have lost your pass, but I shall give you a letter to the doctor that you can show if somebody shall stop you. I shall give you a little map also."

"Only one thing," added Mrs. Strauss. "When you come near Henderson, so if anybody ask, you do not belong to Dr. Culpepper. Many there shall know that he has no slaves. Say that you belong to Mr. Strauss and he send you with medicine that the doctor ordered."

"If they ask why we do not use the mail, say we are foreigners—how do you say—eccentric, and you can still show the letter."

171

The rest of the evening was spent in preparations.
Mrs. Strauss filled a large medicine jar with red
candy and pasted labels and warnings all over it
while Mr. Strauss wrote his letter. Then they both
went over the route to Henderson with us. It was a
distance of about thirty miles, and they expected it to
take us two days. They wrote down the names of
some of the places we would pass on the way and we
tried to memorize them.

Then Mrs. Strauss glanced up at the clock.

"Ach! It is eight and a half. You children shall
sleep here on the sofa. I get a blanket."

It was a hot night and we soon kicked off the
blanket, but late at night I heard Mrs. Strauss tiptoe
in and I felt her tucking the blanket around my
shoulders. I almost thought I was back in the cabin
with Mama, and all of a sudden I wanted to cry.

The Strausses were up before us in the morning.
Mrs. Strauss had made us a big breakfast of eggs and
sausages and had stuffed our food sack. Mr. Strauss
was once again checking the "pill" jar, the letter and
the map. At last all was ready. We said good-by and
set off.

That morning I felt for the first time the joy and excitement of the road. The sun was bright and the air warm and soft. The country was green and rolling, and my heart was all grateful and full of hope. Obie whistled as he walked along beside me, and I knew he felt the same.

We were stopped once on the edge of town by a well-dressed young white man. We told him we were buying medicine for our master, and when he had looked at the pills and read Mr. Strauss's letter he shrugged his shoulders and went on his way.

About five miles along the road we were stopped again, this time by a rough-looking man in a farm cart.

"Hey, where d'you think you're going?"

We told the story about the medicine again and showed him the letter. He read it out loud to himself, slowly sounding out the words and following them with a grubby finger:

"Dear Dr. Culpepper, I send the medicine requested by you with these boys. It is already widely used in Europe but difficult to obtain in this country. I would advise a dosage of two pills before breakfast and one before bed. Please inform me of the progress of your patient. Your obedient servant, Joseph Strauss."

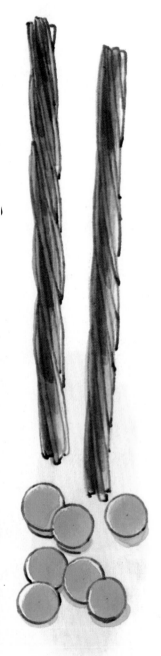

He handed back the letter.

"Wonder what that there medicine's for?"

"Sciatica," answered Obie off the top of his head.

"Sciatica, eh? That's what my old lady complains of. Maybe I'll get some of them pills next time I'm in town."

He started up again, then stopped.

"Where'd you say your master lives—Henderson?"

"Yes, sir."

"Well, jump in the back. I'm going up that way about fourteen miles and I'll give you a lift."

The more you got to know our driver the nicer he seemed to get. By the time he let us off in the middle of the afternoon, we had talked over his wife's sciatica, the awful cost of medicine, the cleverness of his horse, and a lot of other things, and we felt pretty friendly. When we separated he gave us each a stick of licorice. Right away Obie dug into his pocket and fished out a handful of candy that Mrs. Strauss had given him to offer in return. To my horror I saw that it was the same round, red candy that was shining out from the medicine jar. Luckily, our friend wasn't a very noticing person. Or what he noticed was the wrong thing—my face.

"Naw," he told Obie. "You're going to be in trouble with your big brother if you give me any of that candy. Thanks anyway." And he turned into a side road and drove off.

We were only about eleven miles from Henderson now and well rested, with several hours of daylight still ahead of us, so we decided to try to walk straight through without stopping for the night. We made it, too, though we had to walk the last few

miles in the dark. Those last miles were the hardest and slowest. Every sound frightened us, and even the trees, hills and bushes seemed alive and unfriendly. At last we saw the dim shapes of the town ahead of us. By the time we walked down the main street many of the lights were already in upper windows, and in some houses there was no light at all. We carefully followed the Strausses' directions through the town until we came to a large white frame house with a fence around it. By the light of the full moon we were just able to make out the letters on the gate. They spelled out the name we had memorized the night before: Culpepper.

DR. CULPEPPER

We went around to the back door and knocked softly. There was no sound from the dark house. We knocked again louder. There was some movement inside, and a sleepy voice called, "Coming." In a minute the door was opened by a pleasant-faced middle-aged gentleman holding a candle. Even in his nightcap he looked dignified.

175

"What is it, my lads? Who sent you?" he asked.

"Dr. Culpepper?"

"I am he."

"Master Strauss sent us. We're going north."

The doctor looked at us blankly for a moment; then a light dawned.

"Surely you're not alone?" he inquired, peering into the darkness behind us.

"Yes, sir. There's just us."

"Well, come in and welcome," said the doctor.

Once inside he searched about in the larder and soon had two plates of cold meat before us. While we ate he asked us questions and we told him our story. I could see that he was surprised and concerned at our traveling so far alone.

After we had eaten he led us up the back stairs to a small guest room.

"Sleep as late as you wish in the morning," he told us. "You'll have to get used to sleeping during the day and traveling at night."

That night for the first time in our lives we slept between sheets. I can still remember how clean and smooth and rich they felt.

Think about the selection. Finish the drawing on page 167. Then answer the questions.

1. Use your drawing. What is the boys' goal? Why do they want to reach that goal?

2. Use your drawing. Why must the boys work very hard to reach their goal?

3. Which of the problems that the boys face is the most serious? Tell why you think as you do.

4. Why can't the boys simply follow the signs to reach Henderson?

5. How does Mr. Strauss help the boys overcome one of their problems?

6. Why do people like the Strausses help the runaways get to the North?

7. Does this selection belong in this unit about journeys to new lands? Why do you think as you do?

8. Pretend you are Dr. Culpepper. You are determined to get the boys from Henderson to South Hill. Tell a simple plan.

Think and Discuss

WORK IN A GROUP

Determination is the courage to overcome problems. The people who formed and rode the Underground Railroad had determination. Their determination helped to make this country what it is today. Discuss the problems our country faces today. Discuss how determination will help people overcome them. Ask questions about what your classmates say. Talk about the answers.

Focusing on "From Sea to Shining Sea"

▶ Think about the area in which you live. Discuss what makes your region of the country special. Ask questions about what your classmates say.

▶ Look at the title and subtitles in the article. Think about what you know about your region of the country.
  - In what section will your region be discussed?
  - What reasons for settling your region might be discussed in the article?

▶ As you read each section, think about how the land and people of the regions differ. Use this outline form to take notes.

Facts About America
  I.   The Central Plains
  II. The Mountains
  III. The Deserts
  IV. The Coasts

Now turn the page and read the article. Then you will talk about America, a land of variety.

Connections

From Sea to Shining Sea

The new land of the United States seemed a land of promise to many people. People came from many places, across great oceans, north from Mexico, and south from Canada, to settle in the new country. Still other people moved from one part of the United States to another. This is the land these people traveled in their search for land or riches or a new home.

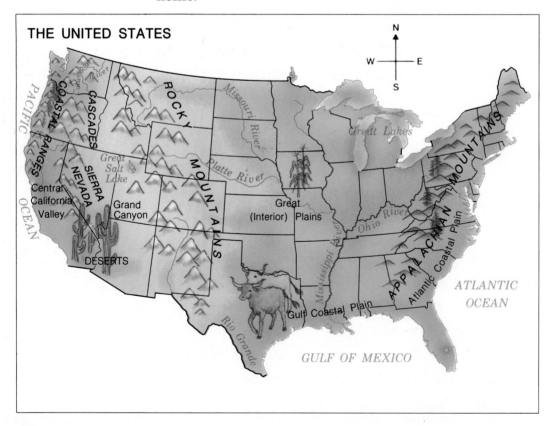

THE UNITED STATES

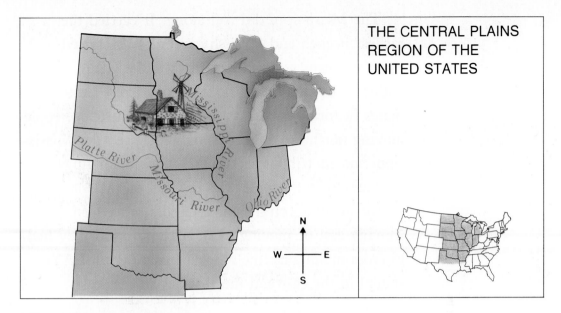

THE CENTRAL PLAINS REGION OF THE UNITED STATES

The Central Plains

Many thousands of people came to settle in the huge middle part of the United States called the **Central Plains.** This area had been explored and claimed by the French and Spanish during the 1500's and 1600's. Two hundred years later, all of this land was part of the United States.

The pioneers who came to this section wanted the land for farming and ranching. Some of the richest farm and grazing land in the world lies in the Central Plains of the United States.

The Plains are watered by one of the world's largest river systems: the Mississippi River and its *tributaries* (TRIB·yuh·tehr·eez), or branch rivers. The Mississippi begins high up in northern Minnesota and flows all the way down to the Gulf of Mexico. In an old folk song, people sang, "Mighty Mississippi, roll along."

The Mississippi did roll along. It carried the earliest French and Spanish explorers. It carried water to farms and ranches all over the Central Plains. It carried boats full of goods from United States factories as well as goods from Europe. People moving north or south, east or west, used the Mississippi and its tributaries to carry their belongings.

Many of the people who crossed the Mississippi settled in the Central Plains. Others moved on. Moving east or moving west, settlers found they had to cross mountains: the Appalachians (AP·uh·LAY· shunz) in the east and the Rockies in the west.

The Mountains

The **Appalachian Highlands** stand between the Central Plains and the East Coast of the United States. The Appalachian Highlands are made up of mountains, steep forested valleys, and low, level lands. Some of the valleys and lowlands have rich farmlands. Other parts of the Appalachian Highlands are rich in coal and petroleum. Some settlers to this area became farmers. Others became miners.

The **Rocky Mountains** stand between the Central Plains and the West Coast of the United States. These mountains are very different from the Appalachian Highlands. The Rocky Mountains, jagged and snow-capped, are among the world's highest mountains.

People who crossed the Rockies told of danger and hardships. Many others died crossing the mountains. They died from the cold, from exhaustion, and

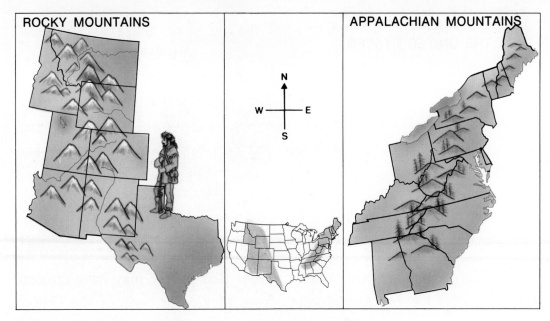

ROCKY MOUNTAINS

APPALACHIAN MOUNTAINS

from hunger. Yet people had to cross the Rockies going west. There was no way around the mountains. The Rocky Mountains stretch all the way from northern New Mexico through Canada and into Alaska.

The Deserts

Many people crossed the desert regions of the United States in their search for land or riches. The desert regions lie west of the Rocky Mountains. The land in this area is very dry and hot with few plants. The **Great Basin** is the largest desert, 200,000 square miles of barren land in California, Idaho, Nevada, Oregon, Utah, and Wyoming.

The **Painted Desert** in Arizona, the **Mojave** (muh·HAHV·ee) **Desert** in California, and the **Sonoran** (suh·NOHR·uhn) **Desert** in Arizona

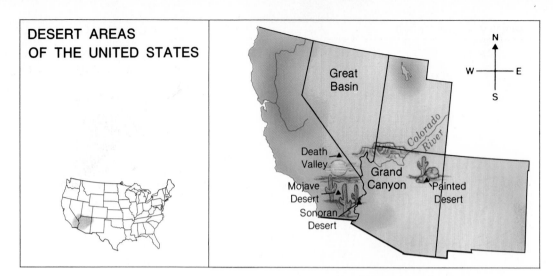

are other desert regions that people may have crossed on their journeys from Mexico or parts of the United States. Just as some people were not prepared for the ruggedness of the Rockies, so others were not prepared for the harshness of the deserts. Many died from the heat or from thirst.

The Coasts

Some of the earliest people to come to the United States sailed from Europe across the Atlantic Ocean. The English and French settled along the Atlantic Coast. The Spanish settled in what is now Florida and along the coast of the Gulf of Mexico. The Spanish then moved across the desert regions to settle in what is now New Mexico, Arizona, and California.

People who came to the Atlantic Coast found flat lands that run along the Atlantic Sea Coast and the Gulf of Mexico. Along the Atlantic Coast, the plains are called the **Atlantic Coastal Plains.**

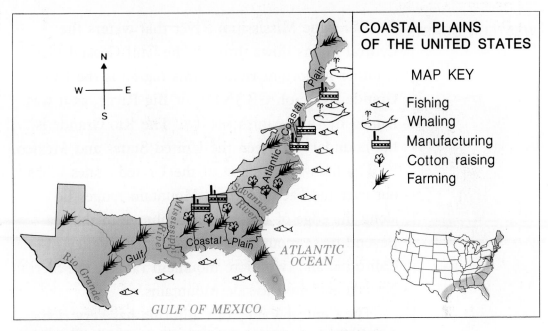

Around the Gulf of Mexico, the plains are called the **Gulf Coastal Plains.**

English colonists who first came to the upper Atlantic Coastal Plains started small farms. The land was not very good for farming, however. The Atlantic Coast had many good *harbors,* places where ships can dock safely. Later colonists turned to fishing, whaling, and shipping.

Many rivers cross the Atlantic Coastal Plains. The rushing waters from the rivers provided power for manufacturing, which started to grow in the middle of the 1880's.

Colonists from France and England settled the lower Atlantic Coastal Plains. The climate there and across the Gulf Coastal Plains ranges from warm to hot, ideal for growing cotton. Great cotton plantations were built where the coastal plain widens in Virginia.

185

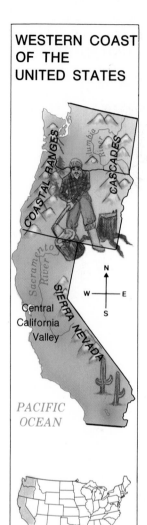

The same Mississippi River that waters the Central Plains flows through the Gulf Coastal Plains. Another important river in this region is the Rio Grande (REE·oh GRAND), or Big River, as it was named by the Spanish settlers. The Rio Grande is the boundary between the United States and Mexico.

The far western coast of the United States looks out over the Pacific Ocean. Mountain ranges lie along the edge of the coast and plunge to the sea. Beyond these mountains lie the Central Valley of California and two more mountain ranges, the Sierra Nevada and the Cascade Mountains.

The Central Valley of California has very rich farmland that is good for growing fruits and vegetables. During the 1840's and 1850's, the discovery of gold led many people to California. It was the rich farmland, however, that made many stay and trade their miners' picks and axes for plows and hoes.

The Sierra Nevada range and the Cascade range extend almost the length of the Pacific Coast from Canada to Mexico. The Cascade Mountains are heavily forested. Settlers to the area now called Washington and Oregon turned to logging. These loggers supplied much of the United States with lumber for homes, furniture, and paper goods.

From east to west, north to south, across mountains and rivers and deserts, people pioneered and settled and built in the United States. By the end of the 1800's, people from all over the world had become Americans living in a proud, young nation that stretched "from sea to shining sea."

Think about the article. Look at the outline you completed as you read. Then answer the questions.

1. Use your outline. Why did people want to settle in your region of the country? What did they find when they arrived?

2. Use your outline. Why did manufacturing grow in the Atlantic Coastal Plains?

3. If you were a farmer in New Hampshire, what might cause you to move westward?

4. Why is it surprising that people now live in the desert? What problems have these people faced?

5. Both gold and rich farmland led people to California. Which reason for settling a new home is better? Tell why you think as you do.

6. This selection is part of a unit about journeying to new lands. Pretend you are a pioneer heading west. What message would you send to a friend back home, telling where you have settled and why?

7. Pretend that you are part of a family from Europe. Tell about all the different land features you want to see in America.

**WORK IN
A GROUP**

The writer refers to the United States as a "land of promise." Discuss what is meant by a "land of promise." Ask questions about what your classmates say. Talk about the answers.

Focusing on "The Great Minu"

▶ Think about a time you traveled to somewhere new. Talk about what happened and how you felt. Ask questions about what your classmates say.

▶ Look at the story pictures. Think about what you know about traveling to somewhere new.

- Which character seems to be traveling to somewhere new? Tell why you think as you do.
- What do you think the traveler will see and learn during the journey?

▶ Get ready to read about what happens to a poor farmer who makes a journey to the big city. As you read, notice what happens to the traveler. Think about what you might add to this time-line drawing.

Farmer
sets off
for the city.

Farmer
returns
to the village.

Now turn the page and read "The Great Minu." Then you will talk about problems talking to and understanding others.

The Great Minu

A West African folk tale retold by Beth P. Wilson

Illustrated by Cheryl Hanna

Since ancient times storytelling has been important throughout the great continent of Africa. Long ago, people in villages would gather together in the evenings and tell stories. Often they would sit in a circle around an open fire. Sometimes one person would begin a story only to have others continue it until the story's end. The tales were both entertaining and clever, often with animals playing tricks on other animals or on people. Usually the wrongdoer was punished in some way.

Some storytellers journeyed from village to village, weaving a magic spell with tales of the tricky hare or the clever spider, and learning new stories as they moved along. Often the listeners would clap their hands, beat on drums, or dance during or after the storytelling.

Today African children are just as excited about telling and listening to folk tales as were their parents and grandparents before them. In West African villages, families often gather in the early evening after a meal of foo-foo *(cooked yam balls dipped in vegetable-beef stew). Soon someone in the group, usually a grandmother, begins a story. Frequently the story is* The Great Minu, *which has long been a favorite of young and old.*

Across the ocean and far away, a poor African farmer prepared to make a journey to the big city of Accra. He walked around his small farm, taking note of the yams and corn growing in the garden. Then he fed his chickens and goats, latched his thatched-roof hut, and took off down the narrow, dusty road.

The farmer hummed happily to himself as the morning sun came into view. How exciting to be going to the big city! Nothing much happened in his tiny village, but since Accra was the largest city in Ghana, he would find much excitement there.

After walking for some time, he stopped to rest under a tulip tree. He leaned against the tree trunk and breathed in the morning air. Birds swooped and soared in the sunshine, but no man, woman, or child traveled the dusty road in either direction.

Soon he jumped to his feet and started down the road again. As he reached the first village along the way, he saw a woman on her knees, washing clothes in a stream of water. "Good day!" he called to the woman. "I'm on my way to the big city—I'm on my way to Accra!" The woman just smiled and went on washing her clothes.

Farther down the road he saw some men and boys making iron. They were too busy to look up when he passed, but he called out just the same. "Good day! I'm on my way to the big city—I'm on my way to Accra!" The men and boys stopped for a moment and nodded. Then they went on working as if he hadn't spoken.

Soon he saw a grandmother telling stories to her little grandchildren. The traveler loved a story and was tempted to stop. But he knew he must be on his way. He waved his hand high and called out, "Good day! I'm on my way to the big city—I'm on my way to Accra!" The children turned to look, and the grandmother smiled and waved. Then she went on telling her story.

The traveler trudged along until he felt tired and hungry. Finding a cool spot, he sat down by the side of the road and opened his lunch bag. He ate a piece of chicken and a big red banana. Then he took a short nap under a cocoa tree.

As soon as the traveler woke up, he started off again because he still had quite a long way to go. At last he approached some farms on the outskirts of Accra. The first thing he noticed was a great herd of cows. He wondered who could own such a herd. Seeing a man with them, he asked, "To whom do these cows belong?"

The man did not know the language of the traveler. So he shrugged his shoulders and said, "Minu," meaning, "I do not understand."

The traveler thought Minu must be a person, and so he exclaimed, "Mr. Minu must be very rich!"

Entering the city, the traveler saw some large new buildings in the town square. He wondered who might own the fine buildings. But the man he asked could not understand his question, so he answered, "Minu."

"Good heavens!" cried the traveler. "What a rich fellow Mr. Minu must be to own all those cows and all these buildings, too!"

Soon he came to a great hotel surrounded by beautiful grounds and mahogany trees. A group of fashionably dressed ladies came down the front steps of the hotel. The traveler stepped up to them and asked who might be the owner of such a grand hotel.

The ladies smiled and said softly, "Minu."

"How wealthy Mr. Minu is!" exclaimed the astonished traveler.

He wandered from one neighborhood to another. Seeing a large house with many columns and porches, he stopped in surprise. "These homes in Accra are so grand—not a bit like the huts of my village," he said.

Just then a servant came out. The traveler stepped up hurriedly and asked, "Please tell me who owns this fine house."

The young woman humped her shoulders. "Minu," she mumbled.

"How foolish of me to ask," the traveler said. "The Great Minu, of course." He stood for a moment, admiring the house and garden. Then he went on.

Finally he came to the harbor, where he saw men loading bananas, cocoa beans, and mahogany onto a huge ship. The blue sky above, the foamy green ocean below, and the sailors rushing about on board ship made quite a sight. Surprised at the great cargo, the traveler inquired of a bystander, "To whom does this fine vessel belong?"

"Minu," replied the puzzled man, who couldn't understand a word the traveler said.

"To the Great Minu also?" the traveler asked. "He is the richest man I ever heard of!"

Just as the traveler was setting out for home, he saw men carrying a coffin down the main street of Accra. A long procession of people, all dressed in black, followed the men. People on the sidelines shook their heads slowly. Sad faces looked up now and then. When the traveler asked one of the mourners the name of the dead person, he received the usual reply, "Minu."

"Mr. Minu is dead?" wailed the traveler. "Poor Mr. Minu! So he had to leave all his wealth—his herd of cows, his buildings, his grand hotel, and his fine ship—and die just like a poor person. Well, well, in the future I'll be content to live a simple life, to breathe the fresh air on my little farm, and to help the poor people in my little village."

The long dusty road back didn't seem as long as it had before. When the farmer arrived home, he unlatched the door of his hut and looked around inside. Then he climbed into his own snug bed and dreamed of the good *foo-foo* he would eat the next day.

Think about the story. Finish the drawing on page 189. Then answer the questions.

Finish the drawing on page 189.

Think and Discuss

1. Use your drawing. The traveler meets many people on the road to Accra. What does he tell them?

2. When the traveler meets the cowherder, what does he ask? What does the man's answer mean?

3. What happens after the meeting with the cowherder? How does this convince the traveler that the Great Minu is the richest man around?

4. What does the reader know that the traveler does not? How is this important to the story?

5. This selection is part of a unit about journeys to new lands. At the end of the story, how does the farmer feel about traveling? How do you know?

6. If you were the traveler, what would you tell your neighbors about the lesson you learned in Accra?

At the United Nations, delegates wear headphones that translate everything they hear into their own languages. Why is good communication important to world peace? Talk about how we can improve our communication with others. Ask questions about what your classmates say. Talk about the answers.

WORK IN A GROUP

TALKING ABOUT THE SELECTIONS

You have read these selections.

Building the Erie Canal

The Erie Canal

Half a Kingdom

Steal Away Home

From Sea to Shining Sea

The Great Minu

Talk about the selections you have read. Consider how the ideas and characters are alike and different. Talk about the theme.

1. How is "The Great Minu" a different kind of story from "Steal Away Home"?

2. How are the two boys going north in "Steal Away Home" like the early settlers who moved west across the United States?

3. Which characters do you think are changed most by their journeys?

4. What do the selections tell you about the reasons people have for setting out on journeys?

BOOKSHELF

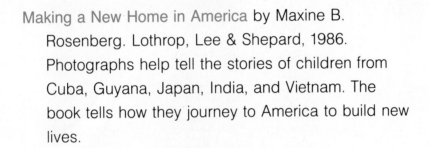

Letters to Horseface: Wolfgang Amadeus Mozart's Journey to Italy 1769–1770 When He Was a Boy of Fourteen by F. N. Monjo. Viking, 1975. A young composer writes humorous letters to his sister, whom he calls Horseface.

Making a New Home in America by Maxine B. Rosenberg. Lothrop, Lee & Shepard, 1986. Photographs help tell the stories of children from Cuba, Guyana, Japan, India, and Vietnam. The book tells how they journey to America to build new lives.

Pioneers on Early Waterways by Edith McCall. Childrens Press, 1980. With a great deal of determination, early settlers made their way to the lands out West by raft, flatboat, barge, and even steamboat.

The Prairie Community by Kathleen Vyn. Messner, 1978. Plant and animal life on the prairie changed when people began to live there. Read about what it was like before the settlers came.

Explorers in a New World by Edith McCall. Childrens Press, 1980. Imagine yourself discovering a new area. Take a look at how some of the people who first explored our land felt.

4 What a Character!

TALKING ABOUT THE THEME

Look at the picture on pages 202 and 203 and read the title.

1. What is a character? What meaning do you think the word has in the title?

2. What characters do you recognize in the picture?

3. Why might these characters stay in your memory?

4. What other unusual characters have you enjoyed reading about? Tell why you think as you do.

5. How do you think the selections in this unit might be alike?

Other Books About Unforgettable Characters

The Mouse on the Motorcycle by Beverly Cleary. William Morrow, 1965. When Ralph the mouse steals Keith's toy motorcycle, it begins a friendship that saves his life.

Pippi Longstocking by Astrid Lindgren. Viking, 1950. Pippi's wild imagination and daring get her into and out of incredible scrapes.

Quentin Corn by Mary Stolz. David Godine Press, 1985. In order to save himself from the butcher, a pig disguises himself as a boy. He runs away, and makes a new life and a valuable friend.

Focusing on "The Escape"

▶ Talk about what it is like to be bored. Ask questions about what your classmates say.

▶ Look at the picture on page 206. Read the first page of the selection. Think about what you know about being bored.
  - What do you think is Wilbur's problem?
  - How might Wilbur solve his problem?

▶ Get ready to read a story about Wilbur and his friends. As you read, think about what happens to Wilbur and how he feels. Think about what you would add to this chart.

Think and Read

What Happens to Wilbur	How He Feels

Now turn the page and read "The Escape." Then you will talk about the good and bad points of being free.

The Escape

From the story *Charlotte's Web* by E. B. White
Illustrated by Garth Williams

Ever since Wilbur, the runt of the pig litter, was given to Fern to raise, he has had constant love and care. He was fed from a bottle, played with, and allowed to follow Fern around like a puppy. The day came, though, when Wilbur had to be sold. Parting from Fern was made a little easier when her uncle Homer Zuckerman agreed to buy him. Wilbur would then be close by, and Fern could walk down the road to visit him in the Zuckerman barn.

One afternoon in June, when Wilbur was almost two months old, he wandered out into his small yard outside the barn. Fern had not arrived for her usual visit. Wilbur stood in the sun feeling lonely and bored.

"There's never anything to do around here," he thought. He walked slowly to his food trough and sniffed to see if anything had been overlooked at lunch. He found a small strip of potato skin and ate it. His back itched, so he leaned against the fence and rubbed against the boards. When he tired of this, he walked indoors, climbed to the top of the manure pile, and sat down. He didn't feel like going to sleep, he didn't feel like digging, he was tired of standing still, tired of lying down. "I'm less than two months old and I'm tired of living," he said. He walked out to the yard again.

"When I'm out here," he said, "there's no place to go but in. When I'm indoors, there's no place to go but out in the yard."

"That's where you're wrong, my friend, my friend," said a voice.

Wilbur looked through the fence and saw the goose standing there.

"You don't have to stay in that dirty-little dirty-little dirty-little yard," said the goose, who talked rather fast. "One of the boards is loose. Push on it, push-push-push on it, and come on out!"

"What?" said Wilbur. "Say it slower!"

"At-at-at, at the risk of repeating myself," said the goose, "I suggest that you come on out. It's wonderful out here."

"Did you say a board was loose?"

"That I did, that I did," said the goose.

Wilbur walked up to the fence and saw that the goose was right—one board was loose. He put his head down, shut his eyes, and pushed. The board gave way. In a minute he had squeezed through the fence and was standing in the long grass outside his yard. The goose chuckled.

"How does it feel to be free?" she asked.

"I like it," said Wilbur. "That is, I *guess* I like it." Actually, Wilbur felt queer to be outside his fence, with nothing between him and the big world.

"Where do you think I'd better go?"

"Anywhere you like, anywhere you like," said the goose. "Go down through the orchard, root up the sod! Go down through the garden, dig up the radishes! Root up everything! Eat grass! Look for corn! Look for oats! Run all over! Skip and dance, jump and prance! Go down through the orchard and stroll in the woods! The world is a wonderful place when you're young."

"I can see that," replied Wilbur. He gave a jump in the air, twirled, ran a few steps, stopped, looked all around, sniffed the smells of afternoon, and then set off walking down through the orchard. Pausing in the shade of an apple tree, he put his strong snout into the ground and began pushing, digging, and rooting. He felt very happy. He had plowed up quite a piece of ground before anyone noticed him. Mrs. Zuckerman was the first to see him. She saw him from the kitchen window, and she immediately shouted for the men.

"Ho-*mer*!" she cried. "Pig's out! Lurvy! Pig's out! Homer! Lurvy! Pig's out. He's down there under that apple tree."

"Now the trouble starts," thought Wilbur. "Now I'll catch it."

The goose heard the racket and she, too, started hollering. "Run-run-run downhill, make for the woods, the woods!" she shouted to Wilbur. "They'll never-never-never catch you in the woods."

The cocker spaniel heard the commotion and he ran out from the barn to join the chase. Mr. Zuckerman heard, and he came out of the machine shed where he was mending a tool. Lurvy, the hired man, heard the noise and came up from the asparagus patch where he was pulling weeds. Everybody walked toward Wilbur and Wilbur didn't know what to do. The woods seemed a long way off, and anyway, he had never been down there in the woods and wasn't sure he would like it.

"Get around behind him, Lurvy," said Mr. Zuckerman, "and drive him toward the barn! And take it easy—don't rush him! I'll go and get a bucket of slops."

The news of Wilbur's escape spread rapidly among the animals on the place. Whenever any creature broke loose on the Zuckermans' farm, the event was of great interest to the others. The goose shouted to the nearest cow that Wilbur was free, and soon all the cows knew. Then one of the cows told one of the sheep, and soon all the sheep knew. The lambs learned about it from their mothers. The horses, in their stalls in the barn, pricked up their ears when they heard the goose hollering; and soon the horses had caught on to what was happening. "Wilbur's out," they said. Every animal stirred and lifted its head and became excited to know that one of his friends had got free and was no longer penned up or tied fast.

Wilbur didn't know what to do or which way to
run. It seemed as though everybody was after him.
"If this is what it's like to be free," he thought, "I
believe I'd rather be penned up in my own yard."

The cocker spaniel was sneaking up on him from
one side, Lurvy the hired man was sneaking up on
him from the other side. Mrs. Zuckerman stood
ready to head him off if he started for the garden,
and now Mr. Zuckerman was coming down toward
him carrying a pail. "This is really awful," thought
Wilbur. "Why doesn't Fern come?" He began to cry.

The goose took command and began to give
orders.

"Don't just stand there, Wilbur! Dodge about,
dodge about!" cried the goose. "Skip around, run
toward me, slip in and out, in and out, in and out!
Make for the woods! Twist and turn!"

The cocker spaniel sprang for Wilbur's hind leg. Wilbur jumped and ran. Lurvy reached out and grabbed. Mrs. Zuckerman screamed at Lurvy. The goose cheered for Wilbur. Wilbur dodged between Lurvy's legs. Lurvy missed Wilbur and grabbed the spaniel instead. "Nicely done, nicely done!" cried the goose. "Try it again, try it again!"

"Run downhill!" suggested the cows.

"Run toward me!" yelled the gander.

"Run uphill!" cried the sheep.

"Turn and twist!" honked the goose.

"Jump and dance!" said the rooster.

"Look out for Lurvy!" called the cows.

"Look out for Zuckerman!" yelled the gander.

"Watch out for the dog!" cried the sheep.

"Listen to me, listen to me!" screamed the goose.

Poor Wilbur was dazed and frightened by this hullabaloo. He didn't like being the center of all this fuss. He tried to follow the instructions his friends were giving him, but he couldn't run downhill and uphill at the same time, and he couldn't turn and twist when he was jumping and dancing, and he was crying so hard he could barely see anything that was happening. After all, Wilbur was a very young pig—not much more than a baby, really. He wished Fern were there to take him in her arms and comfort him. When he looked up and saw Mr. Zuckerman standing quite close to him, holding a pail of warm slops,

he felt relieved. He lifted his nose and sniffed. The smell was delicious—warm milk, potato skins, wheat middlings, Kellogg's Corn Flakes, and a popover left from the Zuckermans' breakfast.

"Come, pig!" said Mr. Zuckerman, tapping the pail. "Come pig!"

Wilbur took a step toward the pail.

"No-no-no!" said the goose. "It's the old pail trick, Wilbur. Don't fall for it, don't fall for it! He's trying to lure you back into captivity-ivity. He's appealing to your stomach."

Wilbur didn't care. The food smelled appetizing. He took another step toward the pail.

"Pig, pig!" said Mr. Zuckerman in a kind voice, and began walking slowly toward the barnyard, looking all about him innocently, as if he didn't know that a little white pig was following along behind him.

"You'll be sorry-sorry-sorry," called the goose.

Wilbur didn't care. He kept walking toward the pail of slops.

"You'll miss your freedom," honked the goose. "An hour of freedom is worth a barrel of slops."

Wilbur didn't care.

When Mr. Zuckerman reached the pigpen, he climbed over the fence and poured the slops into the trough. Then he pulled the loose board away from the fence, so that there was a wide hole for Wilbur to walk through.

"Reconsider, reconsider!" cried the goose.

Wilbur paid no attention. He stepped through the fence into his yard. He walked to the trough and took a long drink of slops, sucking in the milk hungrily and chewing the popover. It was good to be home again.

While Wilbur ate, Lurvy fetched a hammer and some 8-penny nails and nailed the board in place. Then he and Mr. Zuckerman leaned lazily on the fence and Mr. Zuckerman scratched Wilbur's back with a stick.

"He's quite a pig," said Lurvy.

Think about the selection. Finish the chart on page 205. Then answer the questions.

1. Use your chart. At the beginning of the story, what is Wilbur's problem? How does he try to solve it?

2. Use your chart. What character tries to get Wilbur to escape from the barnyard? Why do you think this character does this?

3. How does Wilbur feel when he first gets out of the barnyard? What happens to change his feelings?

4. Use your chart. Think about Wilbur's barnyard life. Think about what happens to him after he escapes. Which kind of activity do you think is more exciting? Why does Wilbur decide to go back?

5. Pretend this story had an ordinary pig as the main character. Would the story belong in a unit about unusual characters? Tell why or why not.

6. Think about the whole story. What might have happened to make Wilbur decide not to go back to the barnyard?

**WORK IN
A GROUP**

Talk about the responsibility that comes with being free. Share your ideas with your classmates. Ask questions about what your classmates say. Talk about the answers.

"Memories"
Think and Read
Think and Discuss

Focusing on "Four Fearsome Critters"

▶ Think about a time you saw something in the dark that was not really there. Discuss with your classmates what happened. Ask questions about what your classmates say.

▶ Read the title and look at the pictures on pages 218 and 219. Think about what you know about seeing things in the dark that are not really there.
  ● What can you tell about what you will read from the pictures and title?
  ● Where do you think these critters can be found?

▶ Get ready to read about four fearsome critters. As you read, think about what makes each critter different. Think about what you would add to this chart.

Critter's Name	Where It Lives	What It Does

Now turn the page and read "Four Fearsome Critters." Then you will talk about critters from the imagination.

217

Four Fearsome Critters

Folklore collected by Alvin Schwartz
Illustrated by Ed Taber

It is said that there are strange creatures
all around us—
    in the woods,
        in the mountains,
           in the lakes,
               everywhere.
Ranchers, woodcutters, hunters, and other people
see these creatures again and again.
Or so they say.
Here is what they tell of them.

hide-behind

When a hunter enters the deepest woods
and does not come back,
most people say the hunter got lost.
But some say the hunter was grabbed
by a hide-behind
that hid behind a tree.

218

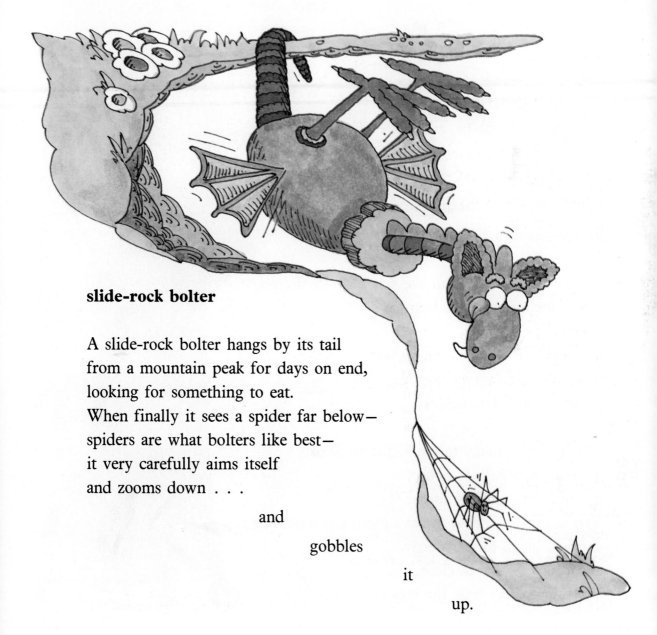

slide-rock bolter

A slide-rock bolter hangs by its tail
from a mountain peak for days on end,
looking for something to eat.
When finally it sees a spider far below—
spiders are what bolters like best—
it very carefully aims itself
and zooms down . . .

          and

              gobbles

                  it

                    up.

kickle snifters

Kickle snifters are about the size of your thumb.
They live inside men's beards.
But this gets boring,
and they are forever peeking out.
They also are forever laughing,
because beard hair tickles.

You are most likely to see kickle snifters
at your grandfather's house,
or your great-uncle's house.
You see them when you have eaten too much supper,
and you begin to feel sleepy,
and your eyes try to close,
and things don't look the way they usually do.

220

whing-whang

On nights when the moon
is a giant orange in the sky,
the whing-whang leaps about the beach
and with its tail writes
whing-whang, whing-whang, whing-whang
in the sand.
But when the moon goes down
and the sun comes up,
it rubs out what it has written
and disappears.

A Note from the Author

The creatures in this bestiary live only in our
imaginations. Folklorists classify our folk animals as
"fearsome critters," although most are funny, not
fearsome. One folklorist has said that eighty-one
different kinds of "critters" have been identified. But
clearly there are more.

The next time you are in the woods or anywhere,
look closely and listen carefully. You, too, may see a
fearsome critter.

Think about the selection. Finish the chart on page 217. Then answer the questions.

1. Use your chart and look at the picture of the hide-behind. Why did people invent this critter?

2. Use your chart. Think about the slide-rock bolter. From whose imagination did it come—a rancher's, a woodcutter's, a hunter's, or another person's? Give reasons for your answer.

3. Use your chart. How do you think kickle snifters got their name? Do you think this is a good name for them? Tell why or why not.

4. Close your eyes and use your imagination. Tell what you think the whing-whang looks like.

5. How many critters do you think there are? Give reasons for your answer.

6. This selection is part of a unit about unusual and funny characters. Does the selection belong in this unit? Tell why you think as you do.

**WORK IN
A GROUP**

Talk about imagination. What good things come from imagination? Ask questions about what your classmates say. Talk about the answers.

Focusing on "Folk Heroes of the United States"

▶ Think about your region of the country. Discuss what your home was like long ago. Ask questions about what your classmates say.

▶ Read the title and subtitles on pages 224–230. Look at the pictures. Think about what you know about what your home was like long ago.
  - Which folk hero lived closest to the area in which you live?
  - In what ways are all the heroes similar?

▶ Get ready to read about some folk heroes. As you read, look for bigger-than-life details. Copy this chart. Take notes about each folk tale hero.

Folk Hero's Name	Bigger-Than-Life Details

Now turn the page and read "Folk Heroes of the United States." Then you will talk about folk heroes.

Folk Heroes of the United States

Back in the days when the United States was young, workers amused themselves by swapping tall tales about their favorite heroes. A *tall tale* is a story that may have a *little* bit of truth in it. Then the truth is s-t-r-e-t-c-h-e-d beyond belief to make a story that is just plain fun. Every region of the United States has its own tall tales and its own heroes. Here are some tall tales and the regions from which they came.

224

Illustrated by Betsy Day

THE NORTH: Tales of Paul Bunyan

Across the top of Minnesota, Wisconsin, and Michigan is a huge evergreen forest called the North Woods. Cutting down trees for lumber, or *logging,* is an important industry here. In the past, loggers cut down trees with axes and handsaws—a hard, dangerous job. Stories grew up about the great strength and daring of loggers, especially that greatest logger of them all—Paul Bunyan!

Paul Bunyan was the biggest, strongest, toughest logger who ever lived. At birth, Paul weighed 86 pounds. When he was full grown, he was taller than the tallest pine tree.

Paul began logging in Maine. He was so fast at cutting down trees that he soon ran out of woods in that state. So he hired a crew and headed west. Paul and his crew set up camp along the Onion River. Paul's crew, of course, was a *big* crew. It had many men, and the men were *big* (though not as big as Paul). Paul's camp was huge. The tables where the loggers ate were so long that the waiters wore roller skates when they served meals. Paul had to dig the Great Lakes so his men would have plenty of water to drink!

Paul didn't remain at the Onion River camp, however. After logging the North Woods, Paul turned to North Dakota. "Aha!" he thought. "A nice flat state—perfect for growing wheat!" In those days, however, North Dakota was covered with trees so tall that it took a week to see up to their tops. In no time at all, Paul Bunyan had cut down those trees and pounded their stumps right into the ground!

THE SOUTH: Tales of John Henry

While loggers in the North swapped tales about Paul Bunyan and his mighty axe, "steel-drivin' men" in the South boasted of John Henry and his mighty hammer. "Steel-drivin' men" were railroad workers who had the most dangerous job of all—blasting through mountains to make railroad tunnels. To do this job, they drove long steel rods deep into solid rock to make holes for dynamite. Those holes had to be about seven feet deep!

Some people say there really *was* a John Henry.
They say he was a "steel-drivin' man" of great size
and strength. John Henry worked for the Chesapeake
and Ohio Railroad in West Virginia during the
1870s. Through the years the tales that were told
about him grew taller and taller.

People in the South say that when John Henry
was born, lightning split the air. The earth shook,
and the Mississippi River ran upstream 1,000 miles.
John Henry weighed 44 pounds when he was born.
After his first meal, he went looking for work. He
got a job with the C&O Railroad, laying track and
blasting tunnels.

People say that John Henry died a hero's death. His crew had put him against a steam drill in a steel-driving race. John Henry won—but he died that night of a burst blood vessel.

THE EAST: Tales of Stormalong

In the late 1700s, New England's seaports were busy places. At about this time New England sailors began telling tales about a sailor named Alfred Bulltop Stormalong. Old Stormalong, or Stormy as he was called, was a daring and skillful sailor. It was

even said that he was born with ocean water flowing through his veins.

Like Paul Bunyan and John Henry, Old Stormalong was a huge man. Old Stormy was as tall as a whale standing on end. Only one ship was big enough for him. That was the *Courser*. The *Courser* was so big that it took a person 24 hours to make the trip from front to back on horseback. The ship's masts were so tall that they were hinged to let the sun and moon pass by.

One day, Stormalong and his crew were fishing in the Atlantic Ocean. The captain decided it was time to move on. He ordered them to pull up the anchor and set sail. The crew could not make the anchor move. Old Stormy jumped overboard to take a look. He found a giant squid holding the anchor in fifty of its slimy arms. The squid's other fifty arms grabbed the sea bottom. A huge fight took place. When the water cleared, the anchor was free. Stormalong had tied every one of the squid's hundred arms into a double knot.

THE WEST: Tales of Pecos Bill and Slue-Foot Sue

In the days of the Old West, cowhands drove cattle a long way to market. At night they would gather around the campfire and tell stories about Pecos Bill and his bride Slue-Foot Sue. Pecos Bill was raised by a coyote and taught by a grizzly bear.

Pecos Bill went on to teach ranchers a thing or two. It was Pecos Bill who invented the lasso, cattle branding, the cattle roundup, and the rodeo. He was perhaps the most remarkable man who ever rode the range.

Slue-Foot Sue, Bill's bride, was remarkable, too. It was love at first sight when Bill saw Sue riding a catfish the size of a whale down the Rio Grande. Sue and Bill raised a large family. They even adopted a litter of coyote pups. People said the pups were so smart that two of them were elected to Congress!

Think about the selection. Look at the chart you completed as you read. Then answer the questions.

1. Use your chart. How are all of the folk heroes alike?

2. Use your chart. Think about Stormy. What flowed in his veins instead of blood? What does this tell you about him?

3. Why did telling tall tales about Pecos Bill make cowhands' lives easier?

4. Some people say there was a real John Henry. Which parts of his story could be real? Which parts are bigger than life?

5. How is a tall tale different from other stories? Why do you think people tell tall tales?

6. Pretend the characters in this selection did not do bigger-than-life things. Would this selection belong in a unit about funny and unusual characters? Tell why or why not.

7. Think of a job that early Americans found difficult. What bigger-than-life things could make this job easier?

Think and Discuss

Folk heroes came to life because of the difficult jobs early Americans faced. Talk about what a modern folk hero would be like. What work might a modern folk hero do? What details could be exaggerated in a folk tale about that hero? Ask questions about what your classmates say.

Focusing on "Spunky Ramona"

▶ Think about when you were in first grade. Talk about what being in first grade is like. Ask questions about what your classmates say.

▶ Read the title and introduction on page 234. Think about what you know about being in first grade.
  - Why do you think Ramona hates school at the start of the story?
  - How might Beezus try to help Ramona?

▶ Get ready to read about what happens to Ramona. As you read, think about how Ramona handles each problem she faces. Think about what you would add to this chart.

Problem	What Ramona Does	What Happens

Now turn the page and read "Spunky Ramona."
Then you will talk about growing up.

Spunky Ramona

From the story *Ramona the Brave* by Beverly Cleary
Illustrated by Jennie Williams

Ramona Geraldine Quimby is convinced nobody loves her. Even the family cat, Picky-picky, keeps away from her. Ramona likes being a little different though. She signs her last name with a special Q: , and she can draw better than anyone in her first grade class. Then one day a girl named Susan copies an owl Ramona is drawing, and the teacher, Mrs. Griggs, picks up Susan's owl to praise. Terribly angry, Ramona scrunches up Susan's owl. Later she has to apologize in front of the class. Ramona begins to hate school. If only her older sister Beezus felt the same way!

One afternoon Mrs. Griggs handed each member of Room One a long sealed envelope. "These are your progress reports for you to take home to your parents," she said.

Ramona made up her mind then and there that she was not going to show any progress report to her mother and father if she could get out of it. As soon as

she reached home, she hid her envelope at the bottom
of a drawer under her summer playclothes. Then she
got out paper and crayons and went to work on the
kitchen table. On each sheet of paper she drew in
black crayon a careful outline of an animal: a mouse
on one sheet, a bear on another, a turtle on a third.
Ramona loved to crayon and crayoning made her
troubles fade away. When she had filled ten pages with
outlines of animals, she found her father's stapler and
fastened the paper together to make a book. Ramona

could make an amazing number of things with paper, crayons, staples, and Scotch tape. Bee's wings to wear on her wrists, a crown to wear on her head, a paper catcher's mask to cover her face.

"What are you making?" asked her mother.

"A coloring book," said Ramona. "You won't buy me one."

"That's because the art teacher who talked to the P.T.A. said coloring books were not creative. She said children needed to be free and creative and draw their own pictures."

"I am," said Ramona. "I am drawing a coloring book. Howie has a coloring book, and I want one too."

"I guess Howie's mother missed that meeting." Mrs. Quimby picked up Ramona's coloring book and studied it. "Why, Ramona," she said, sounding pleased, "you must take after your father. You draw unusually well for a girl your age."

"I know." Ramona was not bragging. She was being honest. She knew her drawing was better than most of the baby work done in Room One. So was her printing. She went to work coloring her turtle green, her mouse brown. Filling in outlines was not very interesting, but it was soothing. Ramona was so busy that by dinnertime she had forgotten her hidden progress report.

Ramona forgot until Beezus laid her long white envelope on the table after the dessert of canned peaches and store macaroons. "Mr. Cardoza gave us our progress reports," she announced.

Mr. Quimby tore open the envelope and pulled out the yellow sheet of paper. "M-m-m. Very good, Beezus. I'm proud of you."

"What did he say?" Beezus asked. Ramona could tell that Beezus was eager to have the family hear the nice things Mr. Cardoza had to say about her.

"He said, 'Beatrice has shown marked improvement in math. She is willing and a conscientious pupil, who gets along well with her peers. She is a pleasure to have in the classroom.' "

"May I please be excused?" asked Ramona and did not wait for an answer.

"Just a minute, young lady," said Mr. Quimby.

"Yes, what about your progress report?" asked Mrs. Quimby.

"Oh . . . that old thing," said Ramona.

"Yes, that old thing." Mr. Quimby looked amused, which annoyed Ramona. "Bring it here," he said.

Ramona faced her father. "I don't want to."

Mr. Quimby was silent. The whole family was silent, waiting. Even Picky-picky, who had been washing his face, paused, one paw in the air, and waited. Ramona turned and walked slowly to her room and slowly returned with the envelope. Scowling, she thrust it at her father who tore it open.

"Does Beezus have to hear?" she asked.

"Beezus, you may be excused," said Mrs. Quimby. "Run along and do your homework."

Ramona knew that Beezus was in no hurry to run along and do her homework. Beezus was going to listen, that's what Beezus was going to do. Ramona scowled more ferociously as her father pulled out the sheet of yellow paper.

"If you don't look out, your face might freeze that way," said Mr. Quimby, which did not help. He studied the yellow paper and frowned. He handed it to Mrs. Quimby, who read it and frowned.

"Well," said Ramona, unable to stand the suspense, "what does it say?" She would have grabbed it and tried to read it herself, but she knew it was written in cursive.

Mrs. Quimby read, " 'Ramona's letter formation is excellent, and she is developing good word-attacking skills.' "

Ramona relaxed. This did not sound so bad, even though she had never thought of reading as attacking words. She rather liked the idea.

Mrs. Quimby read on. " 'She is learning her numbers readily.' "

That mitten counting, thought Ramona with scorn.

" 'However, Ramona sometimes shows more interest in the seatwork of others than in her own. She needs to learn to keep her hands to herself. She also needs to work on self-control in the classroom.' "

"I do not!" Ramona was angry at the unfairness of her teacher's report. What did Mrs. Griggs think she had been working on? She hardly ever raised her hand anymore, and she never spoke out the way she used to. And she wasn't really interested in Davy's seatwork. She was trying to help him because he was having such a hard time.

"Now, Ramona." Mrs. Quimby's voice was gentle. "You must try to grow up."

Ramona raised her voice. "What do you think I'm doing?"

"You don't have to be so noisy about it," said Mr. Quimby.

Of course, Beezus had to come butting in to see what all the fuss was about. "What did Mrs. Griggs say?" she wanted to know, and it was easy to see she knew that what Mr. Cardoza had said was better.

"You mind your own business," said Ramona.

"Ramona, don't talk that way." Mr. Quimby's voice was mild.

"I will *too* talk that way," said Ramona. "I'll talk any way I want!"

"Ramona!" Mr. Quimby's voice held a warning.

Ramona was defiant. "Well, I will!" Nothing could possibly get any worse. She might as well say anything she pleased.

"Now see here, young lady—" began Mr. Quimby.

Ramona had had enough. She had been miserable the whole first grade, and she no longer cared what happened. She wanted to do something bad. She wanted to do something terrible that would shock her whole family, something that would make them sit up and take notice. "I'm going to say a bad word!" she shouted with a stamp of her foot.

That silenced her family. Picky-picky stopped washing and left the room. Mr. Quimby looked surprised and—how could he be so disloyal?—a little amused. This made Ramona even angrier. Beezus looked interested and curious. After a moment Mrs. Quimby said quietly, "Go ahead, Ramona, and say the bad word if it will make you feel any better."

Ramona clenched her fists and took a deep breath. "Guts!" she yelled. "*Guts! Guts! Guts!*" There. That should show them.

Unfortunately, Ramona's family was not shocked and horrified as Ramona had expected. They laughed. All three of them laughed. They tried to hide it, but they laughed.

"It isn't funny!" shouted Ramona. "Don't you dare laugh at me!" Bursting into tears, she threw herself face down on the couch. She kicked and she pounded the cushions with her fists. Everyone was against her. Nobody liked her. Even the cat did not like her. The room was silent, and Ramona had the satisfaction of knowing she had stopped their laughing. She heard responsible old Beezus go to her room to do her responsible old homework. Her parents continued to sit in silence, but Ramona was past caring what anyone did. She cried harder than she ever had cried in her life. She cried until she was limp and exhausted.

Then Ramona felt her mother's hand on her back. "Ramona," she said gently, "what are we going to do with you?"

With red eyes, a swollen face, and a streaming nose, Ramona sat up and glared at her mother. "Love me!" Her voice was fierce with hurt. Shocked at her own words, she buried her face in the pillow. She had no tears left.

"Dear heart," said Mrs. Quimby. "We *do* love you."

Ramona sat up and faced her mother, who looked tired, as if she had been through many scenes with Ramona and knew many more lay ahead. "You do

not. You love Beezus.'' There. She had said it right out
loud. For years she had wanted to tell her parents how
she felt.

Mr. Quimby wiped Ramona's nose on a Kleenex,
which he then handed to her. She clenched it in her
fist and glowered at her parents.

"Of course we love Beezus," said Mrs. Quimby.
"We love you both."

"You love her more," said Ramona. "A whole lot
more." She felt better for having said the words,
getting them off her chest, as grown-ups would say.

"Love isn't like a cup of sugar that gets used up,"
said Mrs. Quimby. "There is enough to go around.
Loving Beezus doesn't mean we don't have enough
love left for you."

"You don't laugh at Beezus all the time," said Ramona.

"They used to," said Beezus, who was unable to stay away from this family discussion. "They always laughed at the funny things I did, and it used to make me mad."

Ramona sniffed and waited for Beezus to continue.

Beezus was serious. "Like the time when I was about your age and thought frankincense and myrrh were something the three Wise Men were bringing to the baby Jesus to put on his rash like that stuff Mom used on you when you were a baby. Mom and Dad laughed, and Mom told all her friends, and they laughed too."

"Oh, dear," said Mrs. Quimby. "I had no idea I upset you that much."

"Well, you did," said Beezus, still grumpy over the memory. "And there was the time I thought toilet water was water out of the toilet. You practically had hysterics."

"Now you're exaggerating," said Mrs. Quimby.

Comforted by this unexpected support from her sister, Ramona scrubbed her face with her soggy Kleenex. "Mama, if you really do love me, why do I have to go to school?" At the same time she wondered how she could find out what frankincense and myrrh were without letting anyone know of her ignorance. She had always thought in a vague sort of way that they were something expensive like perfume done up in an extra-fancy Christmas wrapping.

"Ramona, everyone has to go to school," Mrs. Quimby answered. "Loving you has nothing to do with it."

"Then why can't I be in the other first grade, the one in Room Two?" Ramona asked. "Mrs. Griggs doesn't like me."

"Of course she likes you," contradicted Mrs. Quimby.

"No, she doesn't," said Ramona. "If she liked me, she wouldn't make me tell Susan in front of the whole class that I was sorry I scrunched her owl, and she would ask me to lead the Pledge Allegiance. And she wouldn't say bad things about me on my progress report."

"I told you Mrs. Griggs was great on apologies," Beezus reminded her family. "And she will get around to asking Ramona to lead the flag salute. She asks everybody."

"But Beezus, you got along with Mrs. Griggs when you had her," said Mrs. Quimby.

"I guess so," said Beezus. "She wasn't my favorite teacher, though."

"What was wrong with her?" asked Mrs. Quimby.

"There wasn't anything really wrong with her, I guess," answered Beezus. "She just wasn't very exciting is all. She wasn't mean or anything like that. We just seemed to go along doing our work, and that was it."

"Was she unfair?" asked Mrs. Quimby.

Beezus considered the question. "No, but I was the kind of child she liked. You know . . . neat and dependable."

"I bet you never wasted paste," said Ramona, who was not a paste waster herself. Too much paste was likely to spoil a piece of artwork.

"No," admitted Beezus. "I wasn't that type."

Ramona persisted. "*Why* can't I change to Room Two?"

Mr. Quimby took over. "Because Mrs. Griggs is teaching you to read and do arithmetic, and because the things she said about you are fair. You do need to learn self-control and to keep your hands to yourself. There are all kinds of teachers in the world just as there are all kinds of other people, and you must learn to get along with them. Maybe Mrs. Griggs doesn't understand how you feel, but you aren't always easy to understand. Did you ever think of that?"

"Please, Daddy," begged Ramona. "Please don't make me go back to Room One."

"Buck up, Ramona," said Mr. Quimby. "Show us your spunk."

Ramona felt too exhausted to show anyone her spunk, but for some reason her father's order made her feel better. If her mother had said, Poor baby, she would have felt like crying again. Mrs. Quimby led her from the room and, skipping her bath, helped her into bed. Before the light was turned out, Ramona noticed that *Wild Animals of Africa* had been returned to her bookcase.

"Stay with me, Mama," coaxed Ramona, dreading solitude, darkness, and the gorilla in the book. Mrs. Quimby turned off the light and sat down on the bed.

"Mama?"

"Yes, Ramona?"

"Isn't *guts* a bad word?"

Mrs. Quimby thought for a moment. "I wouldn't say it's exactly a bad word. It isn't the nicest word in the world, but there are much worse words. Now go to sleep."

Ramona wondered what could be worse than guts.

Though known for her humorous stories, Beverly Cleary says, "I don't try to be funny. Because of some lucky quirk . . . my stories turn out to be humorous."

Beverly Cleary has written several books about Ramona Quimby and her family. She has also written a series of books about Henry Huggins. Henry, Ramona, and their friends all live in the same imaginary neighborhood. It is much the same as the neighborhood in which Beverly Cleary grew up. The characters in her stories are similar to children she knew, and ideas for her stories often come from events in her own life.

Beverly Cleary didn't enjoy reading until she was eight. Then she went to the library often. After college, she became a librarian. Later, as an author, she wrote the books she had longed to read as a child.

More Books by Beverly Cleary

Ramona Quimby, Age 8
Runaway Ralph
Ralph S. Mouse
Dear Mr. Henshaw

Think about the selection. Finish the chart on page 233. Then answer the questions.

1. Use your chart. What problems does Ramona have to solve?

2. Use your chart. How does Ramona try to solve the problem of the progress report? What does this tell you about Ramona?

3. What do you think is Ramona's biggest problem in this story? What happens to solve the problem?

4. Mr. Quimby tells Ramona to show her spunk. How does a character like *spunky* Ramona fit into this unit about funny and unusual characters?

5. Beezus tells Ramona about problems she faced at her age. Is this a good way to help Ramona? Tell why you think as you do.

6. Pretend you are one of Ramona's parents. How would you help her solve her problems with school?

7. The writer says that Mrs. Quimby looked tired. She knew many more scenes with Ramona lay ahead. What problems might Ramona face as she continues to grow up?

Think and Discuss

Talk about why growing up can be difficult for children. Ask questions about what your classmate says. Talk about the answers.

Focusing on "Paddington Goes to the Hospital"

▶ Talk about what you know about hospitals. Ask questions about what your classmates say.

▶ Read the title and introduction on page 252. Think about what you know about hospitals.

- What kind of trouble could Paddington get into in a hospital?
- Why might Mr. Curry pretend to be hurt?

▶ Get ready to read a play about Paddington. As you read, think about what other characters say. Notice whether or not he understands them. Think about what you would add to this chart.

What a Character Says to Paddington	What Paddington Thinks the Character Means	What the Character Means

Now turn the page and read the play. Then you will talk about misunderstandings.

Paddington Goes to the Hospital

A play by Michael Bond and Alfred Bradley

Illustrated by Tony Kenyon

Paddington, a small brown bear from Peru, is always willing to help people. Sometimes this gets him into trouble with the Browns, the kind people who have given him a home. More often, however, Paddington's problems are with the Browns' neighbor Mr. Curry. No matter what happens, if Mr. Curry is involved, Paddington is sure to get the worst of it—until now. For Mr. Curry is in the hospital pretending he hurt his leg, and Paddington finally has a chance to get even.

Characters

Mrs. Brown	Nurse	Mr. Curry
Mrs. Bird	Mr. Heinz	
Paddington	Sir Archibald	

SCENE ONE

The Browns' *sitting room.* Mrs. Brown *is making up a basket of food when* Mrs. Bird *comes in.*

Mrs. Brown: If I see another bunch of grapes, I shall scream. That's the third this week. Not to mention four pots of jam, two dozen eggs, and a jar of calves-foot jelly.

Mrs. Bird: I thought Mr. Curry was supposed to be ill. He seems to have a very healthy appetite.

Mrs. Brown: He says he hurt his leg in the launderette the other day. I don't know how long he'll be in hospital.

Mrs. Bird: If you ask me, Mr. Curry will be coming out of hospital when it suits *him* and not a minute before. He knows when he is on to a good thing. Free board and lodging.

Mrs. Brown: And everybody at his beck and call.

Mrs. Bird: He has a relapse every time the doctor says he is getting better. The ward nurse has given him some strong hints that they're short of beds, but he takes no notice. And I'm certainly not having him staying here.

(Paddington *comes in carrying a letter.*)

Paddington: There's a letter for you, Mrs. Brown. It looks like Mr. Curry's writing.

Mrs. Brown: Yes, I'm afraid you're right. (*She opens the envelope.*)

Mrs. Bird: What does he say?

Mrs. Brown (*Reading*): "Dear Mrs. Brown, My leg is still troubling me. Will you please send some more apples? I didn't like the last lot—they were too sour. Also another cherry cake. P.S. Two cherries were missing from the one you sent last week."

Paddington (*Guiltily*): Perhaps they were a bit loose?

Mrs. Bird (*With meaning*): Perhaps!

Mrs. Brown: "P.P.S. I would like them as soon as possible. Paddington could bring them round to the hospital. . . ." Do you mind taking this parcel to him, Paddington?

Paddington (*Cheerfully*): No. I don't think I've ever been to a hospital before. I wonder if it's like the Daredevil Doctor series on television?

Mrs. Bird: I shouldn't think so for one moment.

Mrs. Brown: There now. It's packed. And I've fixed the cherries *firmly* in the cake this time, so let's hope they don't fall out.

Mrs. Bird: I've packed you some sandwiches and a thermos flask of cocoa. But be careful. It's very hot.

Paddington: Thank you, Mrs. Bird. I won't be long. (*He puts on his hat as he goes out.*)

Mrs. Brown: I do hope we're doing the right thing, letting him go by himself.

Mrs. Bird: I shouldn't worry about that bear. He knows how to look after number one.

Mrs. Brown: It wasn't Paddington I was thinking of. It's the hospital. . . .

SCENE TWO

A small room in the hospital. A Nurse sits at the desk with a telephone. She is finishing a conversation.

Nurse: Yes, Sir Archibald. Very good, Sir Archibald.

(*She replaces the phone as* Paddington *knocks at the door.*)

Nurse: Come in.

Paddington: Good morning.

Nurse: Good morning. Can I help you?

Paddington: I've come to see Mr. Curry.

Nurse (*Looking through a list*): Mr. Curry. . . . Have
you any idea what he does?

Paddington: He grumbles a lot.

Nurse: That doesn't help. I think I'd better pass you
on to the person who deals with inquiries.

Paddington: Thank you very much. Is he the head man?

Nurse: The *head* man. Bless me! Why didn't you say so before? You want the doctor who looks after things up here. (*She taps her head.*)

Paddington: Up here? (*He taps his own head.*)

Nurse: He's what we call the head shrinker.

Paddington: My hat *is* a bit tight. But I don't think I want my head shrunk. Couldn't you stretch my hat instead?

Nurse: Stretch your hat?

Paddington: Yes. If it was a bit bigger, I could carry more sandwiches in it.

Nurse (*Leaning across the desk*): Sandwiches?

Paddington (*Leaning across the desk so that they are nose-to-nose*): Yes, but I would still have to find somewhere for my cocoa.

Nurse (*Alarmed*): There, there. There's nothing to worry about. (*Picks up the phone quickly and dials a number.*) Mr. Heinz, could you come quickly, please? There's a patient who needs you urgently. Thank you. (*Replaces the phone*)

Paddington: Mr. Heinz! I don't want to see Mr. Heinz. I want to see Mr. Curry. I've brought him one of Mrs. Bird's cherry cakes.

Nurse (*Soothingly*): I think you'll find Mr. Heinz much nicer. He'll soon take your worries away. (*Mr. Heinz enters.*) Oh, Mr. Heinz, I'm so glad to see you. (*She looks at Paddington.*) There's the patient. (*She hurries out.*)

Paddington: Patient? Have I got long to wait?

Mr. Heinz: Oh, no, in fact I'll start right away. Just open your coat, please.

Paddington: I'm sorry about the cherry cake.

Mr. Heinz (*Taking off his glasses and staring at Paddington*): You are sorry about the *cherry cake*?

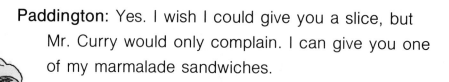

Paddington: Yes. I wish I could give you a slice, but Mr. Curry would only complain. I can give you one of my marmalade sandwiches.

Mr. Heinz (*A slight shudder*): No, thank you. Now, I'd like to play a little game. It's really to test your reactions. (*He sits down in a chair by his desk.*)

Paddington: A game to test my reactions? I didn't know I had any.

Mr. Heinz: Oh, yes. (*He puts his feet up on another chair.*) Everybody has reactions. Some have fast ones and some have slow. (Paddington *sits on his feet.*) Oooh!

Paddington: I'm sorry, Mr. Heinz.

Mr. Heinz: Now I'm going to call out some words— quite quickly—and each time I call one out, I want you to give me another word which has the opposite meaning . . . right?

Paddington (*Promptly, as he settles down in the other chair*): Wrong.

Mr. Heinz: What's the matter? Aren't you comfortable?

Paddington: Oh, yes, but you told me to say the opposite every time you gave me a word.

Mr. Heinz: That wasn't the word, bear! Wait until I give you the go ahead. Once you start I don't want to hear anything else. Ready. . . . Three . . . two . . . one . . . go!

Paddington: Stop!

Mr. Heinz: What's the matter?

Paddington: You said "go" so I said "stop."

Mr. Heinz: Oh. Very good.

Paddington: Very bad.

Mr. Heinz: Look here!

Paddington: Look there! (*A pause*) Can't you think of any more words, Mr. Heinz?

Mr. Heinz (*Drums his fingers on the desk for a moment, then decides to try again*): White.

Paddington: Black.

Mr. Heinz: Big.

Paddington: Small.

Mr. Heinz: Fast.

Paddington: Slow.

Mr. Heinz: Dark.

Paddington: Light.

Mr. Heinz: Fine.

Paddington: Wet.

Mr. Heinz: That's good. We've finished.

Paddington: That's bad. We've started.

Mr. Heinz: No, we haven't!

Paddington: Yes, we have!

Mr. Heinz (*Thumping the table*): No . . . no . . . no!

Paddington (*Thumps the table too, in his excitement*): Yes . . . yes . . . yes!

Mr. Heinz (*Yelling*): Will you stop!

Paddington: Will you go!

Mr. Heinz (*His head in his hands*): Why did I ever take this up? I should have my head examined.

Paddington (*Sitting up*): Perhaps it needs shrinking. I should go and talk to the nurse who was here a few minutes ago. She might be able to help you. She knows all about those things.

(*As* Paddington *gets up,* Mr. Heinz *makes a dash for the door.*)

Mr. Heinz: I shall be gone for five minutes. Five minutes! And if you're still here when I get back, I'll ... I'll . . . (*He hurries out, at a loss for words.*)

Paddington (*Looking round the room*): What a funny hospital. It's not at all like the one in Daredevil Doctor. Hmm. It must be time for lunch. (*He takes a sandwich out.*) I'm glad Mrs. Brown remembered to give me some cocoa. (*He fills the thermos cup and takes a mouthful.*) Ow! (*He hops round the room in agony.*) Ooh! (*He picks up a doctor's bag from the corner of the room, opens it, and examines his tongue in a mirror.*) I knew it. I've blistered my tongue . . . (*He becomes interested in the contents of the bag.*) What's this? (*He puts on a stethoscope and listens to his own heart.*) Hmm. I wonder what it's like to be a doctor.

(*He slips on a white gown and hangs the stethoscope round his neck.*)

Paddington (*Pretending to be a television surgeon*): Nurse! Instruments ready? All right, bring in the patient. (*He puts on his operating mask and paces up and down.*) Now this is serious . . .

(*The Nurse comes in suddenly.*)

Nurse: It certainly is serious. Sir Archibald is coming.

Paddington: Is he?

Nurse: And he's in a terrible mood. You know he doesn't like students who aren't punctual.

Paddington: Student? But I'm not . . .

Nurse: He's here now. I'd say I'm sorry straight away, if I were you.

Sir Archibald (*Storming in*): Ah, there you are.

Paddington: Good morning, Sir Archibald. I'm sorry, Sir Archibald!

Sir Archibald: Sorry? I should think so! Good afternoon's more like it! Now that you *are* here, perhaps you can give us the benefit of your advice. I'd like to have your diagnosis.

Paddington: My diagnosis! (*He begins to unload his basket.*) There's a cherry cake, some eggs, some calves-foot jelly, but I don't think Mrs. Brown packed a diagnosis.

Sir Archibald: Calves-foot jelly. Did you say *calves-foot jelly*?

Paddington: Yes. Grant Dexter says it's very good if you're ill.

Sir Archibald: Grant Dexter! And who might he be?

Paddington: You don't know Grant Dexter? He's the Daredevil Doctor. He's very good at curing people. All his patients get better.

Sir Archibald: Are you suggesting mine don't, Doctor . . . whatever your name is?

Paddington: Doctor? I'm not a doctor, Sir Archibald. (*He pulls off his mask.*) I'm a bear. I've come to visit Mr. Curry.

Sir Archibald (*On the point of exploding*): Curry? Did you say Curry?

Paddington: That's right.

Sir Archibald: Are you a friend of his?

Paddington: Well, I'm not really a friend. He lives next door and I've brought him some food.

Sir Archibald: Food! That's the last thing he needs. It will only make him stay longer. That man's entirely without scruples.

Paddington: Mr. Curry's without scruples! I thought he'd only hurt his leg!

Sir Archibald: Scruples, bear, are things that stop some people taking advantage of others.

Paddington: Oh. I don't think Mr. Curry's got any of those, Sir Archibald. Mrs. Bird's always grumbling because he takes advantage of others.

Sir Archibald: I see. (*Thoughtfully*) Are you any good at tricks, bear?

Paddington: Oh, yes, Sir Archibald. Bears are very good at tricks.

Sir Archibald: I thought you might be. Nurse, wheel Mr. Curry in here. We'll see him privately.

(*The* Nurse *goes and* Sir Archibald *turns to* Paddington.)

Sir Archibald: I think it's time we gave Mr. Curry a surprise—and I think you're the one to give it. Now, if you'll just put your mask back on, bear . . .

Paddington: Yes, Sir Archibald. (*He does.*)

Sir Archibald: I'll give you a chance to see what it's like to be—what did you say his name was?

Paddington: Grant Dexter. The Daredevil Doctor.

Sir Archibald: Now I've an idea. (*He goes to the door and returns with a tool box.*) The workmen left these when they were doing some repairs. When I tell you to get your instruments ready, this is the box I want you to take them from.

Paddington: Right, Sir Archibald.

(Mr. Curry *arrives in a wheelchair pushed by the* Nurse.)

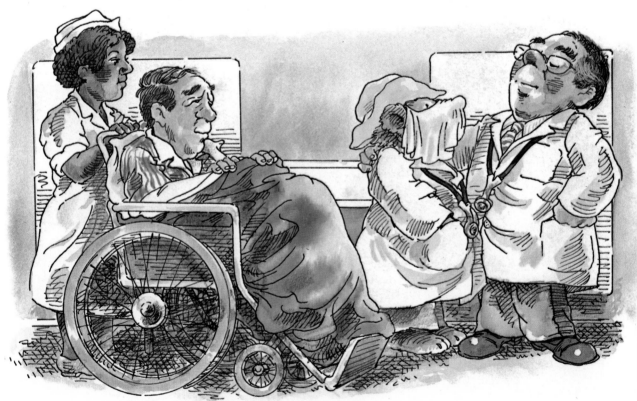

Sir Archibald: Good morning, Mr. Curry. How's the patient today?

Mr. Curry: Oooooooh! Worse, much worse.

Sir Archibald (*Cheerfully*): I thought you might be. That's why we have decided to operate.

Mr. Curry (*Sitting up quickly*): Operate? Did you say operate?

Sir Archibald: Yes, that's right. No good playing around with these things. I'd like to introduce you to . . . a colleague from overseas. He specializes in legs. Does something or other to the knee. Nobody quite knows what, but it seems to work very well in the jungle. Quite a few of his patients still manage to get about more or less. (*To Paddington*) Perhaps you'd like to listen to the patient's heart?

Paddington: Of course, Sir Archibald. (*He sticks the stethoscope under the blanket.*)

Sir Archibald: What can you hear?

Paddington: It's got a very strong beat. (*He jumps up and down to the rhythm.*) I think it's Pick of the Pops.

Mr. Curry: Pick of the Pops! You've got your stethoscope on my transistor radio!

Paddington: I'm sorry, Mr. Curry. (*In his confusion he reverses the stethoscope and puts the headpiece on* Mr. Curry. *He shouts in the other end.*) Are you there?

(Mr. Curry *jumps.*)

Mr. Curry: Of course I am! (*He turns to* Sir Archibald.) Is this . . . this *person* going to be allowed to operate on me? He's not big enough for a start.

Sir Archibald (*Calmly*): Oh, don't worry about his size. We'll give him a box to stand on.

Mr. Curry: A box to stand on!

Sir Archibald: Yes. It may make him a bit wobbly, but it'll be all right.

Mr. Curry: What!

Sir Archibald (*He turns to* Paddington *with a wink.*): Now, if you would just like to get your instruments ready.

Paddington: Certainly, Sir Archibald. (*He opens the carpenter's tool box.*) One hammer . . . (*He puts it on the desk.*)

Mr. Curry: A hammer!

Paddington: One chisel. (*He puts it next to the hammer.*)

Mr. Curry: A chisel!

Paddington: And one saw. (*He brings out a large carpenter's saw.*)

Mr. Curry: A saw!

Sir Archibald: How about something to put him to sleep with, nurse?

(*The* Nurse *hands* Paddington *an enormous mallet.*)

271

Mr. Curry: I'm off. (*He leaps out of the chair.*)

Sir Archibald: Ah, Mr. Curry, I'm glad you're feeling better. You can leave the hospital today.

Mr. Curry: Leave? I don't know what you're talking about.

Sir Archibald: You aren't limping any more, Mr. Curry. In fact, I would say you are completely cured.

Mr. Curry (*Realizes he's been beaten*): Bah! (*He storms out.*)

Sir Archibald (*After his laughter has subsided*): It seems we have another free bed in the ward after all, nurse. (*He removes Paddington's mask and shakes his paw warmly.*) Congratulations, bear. I've never in all my life seen a patient recover so quickly. Perhaps you would like to keep your stethoscope as a souvenir?

Paddington: Thank you very much, Sir Archibald. (*He picks up his basket.*) Would you like some of this cake? I don't suppose Mr. Curry will be needing it now.

Sir Archibald: Mmm. It does seem rather a pity to waste it. (*He looks over his shoulder to make sure the nurse can't hear and then lowers his voice.*) Do you like the cherries?

Paddington (*Lowers his voice too*): I think they're the best part. Except Mrs. Bird's put them on extra tightly this time.

Sir Archibald (*Reaches for the tool box*): I don't doubt we'll find something to lever them off with. (*He hands* Paddington *a suitable tool.*) After you . . .

Paddington: No, after you, Sir Archibald. (*Together, they dig into the basket.*)

(*Curtain*)

Michael Bond, creator of Paddington the bear, is an English writer. He lives with his wife and his daughter in a small town near London, England.

At first Mr. Bond wrote stories, articles, and plays for adults. Then one Christmas Eve he bought a small toy bear. "I saw it left on a shelf of a London store, felt sorry for it, and named it Paddington," he said. As a result, he wrote his first children's book, *A Bear Called Paddington.*

Michael Bond has created other animal characters, too—a mouse called Thursday, and a guinea pig called Olga da Polga. "I like writing about animals," Mr. Bond says. "They sometimes seem more real to me than people. They can also get away with things people never could."

More Books by Michael Bond

Paddington Takes to TV
Paddington Takes the Test
Paddington on Screen
The Complete Adventures of Olga da Polga

Think about the play. Finish the chart on page 251.
Then answer the questions.

1. This play is part of a unit about funny and unusual characters. Who is the most unusual character in this play? Tell why you think as you do.

2. Use your chart. Why is Paddington unhappy about seeing the head shrinker?

3. Use your chart. Why does Mr. Heinz get confused when he tries to test Paddington's reactions? Why does Paddington get confused?

4. Why is Sir Archibald angry when he learns that Paddington has brought food for Mr. Curry?

5. What trick is played on Mr. Curry? Do you think the trick is fair? Tell why you think as you do.

6. Mr. Curry tries to take advantage of Paddington. What is it about Paddington that makes it difficult to take advantage of him?

Talk about misunderstandings. Are all misunderstandings funny? How can misunderstandings be dangerous? Ask questions about what your classmates say. Talk about the answers.

WORK IN A GROUP

Learn About
PLATS

The theater lights dim. The curtain goes up. You are about to see a play. As the actors move and speak, you find out what is happening. With the costumes and scenery, you picture the time and place.

A play is meant to be performed. That is the main difference between a play and a story. When it is written, a play *looks* different, too. It has

a cast of characters

Characters	Mrs. Brown Mrs. Bird	Paddington Nurse

stage directions

(Paddington *comes in carrying a letter.*)

dialogue

Paddington: There's a letter for you, Mrs. Brown. It looks like Mr. Curry's writing.

Mrs. Brown: Yes, I'm afraid you're right.

276

How does a story look different from a play?

1 Does it have characters?

2 Does it have stage directions?

3 Does it have dialogue?

You will find this bear's answers below.

1. A story *does* have characters, but they are not listed at the beginning in a cast of characters.

2. A story *does not* have stage directions, but it *does* tell what the characters do and how they feel. This information is not in parentheses.

3. A story *does* have dialogue, but the dialogue is usually in quotation marks.

REMEMBER!

The <u>cast of characters</u> lists the names of the characters in the play.

The <u>stage directions</u> tell what the characters do and how they speak.

The <u>dialogue</u> is what the characters say.

Read the fable of "The North Wind and the Sun." Be ready to change some of this fable into a play.

The North Wind and the Sun

One day the North Wind boasted to the Sun, "I am much stronger than you." The Sun smiled and replied, "Don't be so sure. *I* may be stronger than *you*." Just then a traveler wrapped in a cloak came walking down the road. "Let's have a contest," said the Sun. "Whoever can make that traveler take off her cloak is the stronger. You may try first."

The North Wind blew as hard as he could upon the traveler. "Who-o-o-o," he howled. The traveler only wrapped the cloak more tightly than ever around her

278

shoulders, and said, "I'm glad I wore my cloak. That north wind is *cold!*"

Then the Sun said, "Now it's my turn." She shone so brightly that the traveler began to feel warm. The traveler smiled and said, "Thank you, Sun," and she took off her cloak as she sat down to rest. "Kindness works better than force," explained the Sun to the North Wind.

On a piece of paper, write the cast of characters for the play of "The North Wind and the Sun." Then read the beginning of the play below and write the next line of dialogue for the Sun. Change the rest of the fable into a play if you wish.

Characters

North Wind *(Boasting)*: I am much stronger than you.

Sun *(Smiling)*: Don't be so sure. I may be stronger than <u>you.</u>

(A traveler wrapped in a cloak comes walking down the road.)

Sun:

TALKING ABOUT THE SELECTIONS

You have read these selections.

The Escape

Four Fearsome Critters

Folk Heroes of the United States

Spunky Ramona

Paddington Goes to the Hospital

Talk about the selections you have read. Consider how the ideas and characters are alike and different. Talk about the theme.

1. How are Paddington and Ramona alike? How are they different?

2. How do you think Wilbur's adventure would have turned out if he had been more like Ramona?

3. Compare Paddington to a folk hero. How are they alike and different?

4. Which character in this unit will you remember best? Tell why.

BOOKSHELF

Where the Sidewalk Ends by Shel Silverstein. Harper & Row, 1974. All kinds of characters, feelings, and events fill these poems that are especially fun, and funny, to read aloud.

Paul Bunyan retold and illustrated by Steven Kellogg. William Morrow, 1984. In this folk tale, the great Paul Bunyan changes the face of America. He begins the greatest logging company ever.

Justin and the Best Biscuits in the World by Mildred and Walter Pitts. Lothrop, Lee & Shepard, 1986. Justin will not help out at home. He is sent to visit his grandfather who has some surprises in store for him.

The Big Cheese by Eve Bunting. Macmillan, 1977. This is a funny story about two very different sisters whose lives are suddenly changed by a big wheel of cheese.

Wingman by Manus Pinkwater. Dodd, Mead, 1975. Donald Chen read comic books all day until he met a Super Hero he called Wingman.

Getting Something on Maggie Marmelstein by Marjorie Weinman Sharmat. Harper & Row, 1971. Thad wants to get something on Maggie. If he does not, she is going to ruin his reputation at school.

5 To Live with Animals

TALKING ABOUT THE THEME

Look at the picture on pages 282 and 283 and read the title.

1. What does the picture show?

2. What do you think the picture has to do with the title?

3. What kind of person would be best at living with animals?

4. What animal would you like to live with? Why?

5. How do you think the selections in this unit will be alike?

Other Books About Animals

Secrets of a Wildlife Watcher by Jim Arnosky. Lothrop, Lee & Shepard, 1983. Discover how to read the clues left by animals to tell how they live.

Animal Fact: Animal Fable by Seymour Simon. Crown, 1979. People have some funny false beliefs about animals. This book tells what you can believe and what you cannot.

Wild Animals, Gentle Women by Margery Facklam. Harcourt Brace Jovanovich, 1978. These true stories tell of eleven women who work with and study animals.

Focusing on "Buying a Puppy"

▶ Talk about why people have pets. Ask questions about what your classmates say.

▶ Read the title of the poem on page 286 and look at the picture. Think about what you know about having pets.
  - What do you think is going on?
  - How do you think the little girl feels?

▶ Get ready to read a poem divided into sections, or stanzas. As you reach each stanza, think about what each character thinks and does. Think about what you might add to this chart.

What Happens?	
Stanza 1	Stanza 6
Stanza 2	Stanza 7
Stanza 3	Stanza 8
Stanza 4	Stanza 9
Stanza 5	Stanza 10

Now turn the page and read "Buying a Puppy." Then you will talk about friendship.

Buying a Puppy

A poem by Leslie Norris

"Bring an old towel," said Pa,
"And a scrap of meat from the pantry.
We're going out in the car, you and I,
Into the country."

I did as he said, although
I couldn't see why he wanted
A scrap of meat and an old towel.
Into the sun we pointed

Our Ford, over the green hills.
Pa sang. Larks bubbled in the sky.
I took with me all my cards—
It was my seventh birthday.

We turned down a happy lane,
Half sunlight, half shadow,
And saw at the end a white house
In a yellow meadow.

Mrs. Garner lived there. She was tall.
She gave me a glass of milk
And showed me her black spaniel.
"Her name is Silk,"

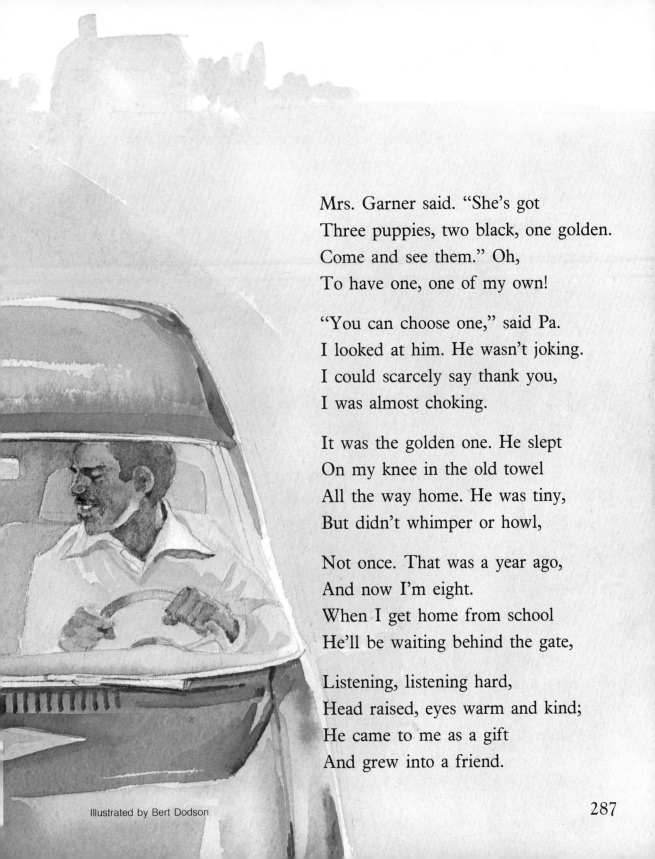

Mrs. Garner said. "She's got
Three puppies, two black, one golden.
Come and see them." Oh,
To have one, one of my own!

"You can choose one," said Pa.
I looked at him. He wasn't joking.
I could scarcely say thank you,
I was almost choking.

It was the golden one. He slept
On my knee in the old towel
All the way home. He was tiny,
But didn't whimper or howl,

Not once. That was a year ago,
And now I'm eight.
When I get home from school
He'll be waiting behind the gate,

Listening, listening hard,
Head raised, eyes warm and kind;
He came to me as a gift
And grew into a friend.

Illustrated by Bert Dodson

287

Think about the poem. Finish the chart on page 285. Then answer the questions.

1. Use your chart. What clue does Pa give the little girl in the first stanza?

2. Use your chart. What special occasion takes place in the poem? How do you know?

3. Use your chart. At what point does the girl become hopeful about getting a puppy as a friend?

4. Why is the girl "almost choking" in stanza 7?

5. What words does the writer use to tell the reader that Mrs. Garner was friendly?

6. What do you think the girl might name her dog? Tell why you think as you do.

7. The selections in this unit are all about people getting along with animals. How does the girl get along with the dog after he is no longer a puppy? What word in stanza 10 tells you how they feel about one another?

WORK IN A GROUP

Tell what friendship means to you. Why is friendship so important? What does it mean to be a friend? Think of a definition of *friendship* on which you can all agree. Share it with the class.

Focusing on "An Allergy Is a Bothersome Thing"

▶ Talk about what you know about allergies. Ask questions about what your classmates say.

▶ Look at the picture on pages 290–291 and read the title. Think about what you know about allergies.
- What do you think is going on?
- How might an allergy be bothersome to the girl in the picture?

▶ Get ready to read a story about a girl with a problem. Every time she tries to solve it, she ends up having a new problem. As you read, think about Beth's actions. Think about what you would add to this chart.

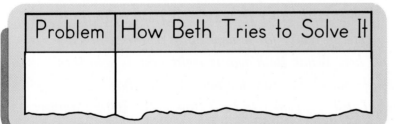

Problem	How Beth Tries to Solve It

Now turn the page and read "An Allergy Is a Bothersome Thing." Then you will talk about loneliness.

289

An Allergy Is a Bothersome Thing

From the novel *Philip Hall likes me. I reckon maybe.* by Bette Greene
Illustrated by Diane de Groat

Lately, things have been changing for Beth Lambert. Her best friend, Philip Hall, has been spending most of his time with other friends, and Beth's family is too busy getting ready for a new baby to think much about her. What Beth wants right now is something special—something just for her. And if that something special just happened to be a dog, *well, Beth Lambert wouldn't mind that at all!*

Mr. Barnes stopped the school bus along the side of the highway just at that spot where the dirt road leading to our farm meets the blacktop. First Philip Hall got off. Then I jumped off in front of the faded black-and-white sign at the intersection which read:

1 mile
↑
Lambert Farm
good turkeys
good pigs

As I took a flying leap across the frozen drainage ditch that separated the road from the field, I heard Philip calling me.

"Hey, Beth!" He was still standing on the blacktop just where the bus left him. "You oughtna be going through the field. You might step into an ice puddle."

Of all days to have to stop and start explaining things to Philip Hall. But at any other time I'd be thinking that he wouldn't be fretting about my feet if he didn't really like me. Now would he? "Frosty feet ain't nothing," I told him, "when you have a spanking new puppy waiting to meet you."

"What if Mr. Grant wouldn't swap a collie dog for one of your pa's turkeys?" asked Philip, grinning as though he hoped it was so.

"That's all you know! When I left the house this morning, my pa was picking out six of our fattest turkeys for swapping." I turned and began running across the field.

"Well, one collie dog is worth more than six of your old turkeys," called Philip.

I kept on running, pretending not to hear. And, anyway, everybody loves to eat turkey. Don't they?

When I reached the rise in the field, I could see our house a nice pale green. As I came closer, I could see my mama on the porch. She was hanging work-worn overalls across the porch clothesline. I tiptoed up behind her and threw my arms around her.

"Ohhh!" She jumped. "What you mean scaring me clear out of my wits, girl?"

"Where is he?" I asked. "Where's the collie?"

She put on her I'm-not-fixing-to-listen-to-any-nonsense face and said, "I don't know nothing about no collie."

"Did Pa make the swap? Did he?"

"Get out of here, girl. Go on into the kitchen."

"Tell me if Pa got the collie," I pleaded. "Now did he?"

Her mouth was still set into that no-nonsense way of hers, but it was different with her eyes. Her eyes were filled up with pure pleasure. "And I told you," she said, "to get on into the kitchen, didn't I?"

Suddenly I understood. I threw open the screen door and, without waiting to close it gently behind me, ran in a straight line through the living room and into the kitchen.

And then I saw him. There in a cardboard carton next to the cookstove was a reddish-brown puppy with a circle of white fluffy hair ringing his neck and spilling down to his chest. I dropped to my knees and showed my open palms. "Hi, puppy. Beautiful little collie puppy."

"He's beautiful, sure enough," said Ma from behind.

The collie just looked at me for a few moments. Then he got to his feet and trotted over.

"And you're friendly too," I said, patting his back. "Hey, that would be a good name for you."

"Friendly," said Ma, smacking her lips like she was word tasting. "That's a right good name."

I gave Friendly a hug and a kiss. "I will now name you— *ah-choo!*" I tried again. "I will now name—*AHHHHhhhh-choo!!*"

Ma shook her head the way she does when she catches me at mischief. "You done gone and got yourself a cold, now, didn't you?"

"*AHHHHhhhhhh-ha-ha-ha-choo!* I now name you Friendly," I said at last.

By bedtime I was sneezing constantly and water kept pouring from my sore, itchy eyes. But, thank goodness, all my sneezing didn't seem to bother Friendly, who slept peacefully in his cardboard carton at the foot of my bed.

I could hear my folks in the kitchen talking about what they were always talking about these days—names for our soon-to-be-born baby. When they finally tired of that topic, Ma said, "Beth got me worried. All them wheezing sounds coming from her chest."

"I seen Doc Brenner in town this afternoon," said Pa. "He asked me to kill and clean one of our twenty-pound birds. Said he'd stop by this evening to pick it up."

"When he comes by," said Ma, "ask him to kindly take a look at our Beth."

I climbed out of bed to take off my raggedy tail of a nightgown and put on the one that Grandma had given me last Christmas. She had made it out of a sack of Fairy Flake flour, but she dyed it a bright, brilliant orange. It was nice.

Friendly started to bark.

"Don't you be frightened, little Friendly. It's only me, only Beth."

While I patted my new pet, I told him how glad I was that he had come to live with us. "You're going to like it here, you'll see. I'm going to bring all my friends to meet you. Philip Hall, Susan, Bon—*ahh-choo-whoo! Ahh choo!* Bonnie, Ginny, Esther. You're going to like all my friends, Friendly, but you're going to like me best of all . . . I reckon maybe."

Ma called out, "Is you out of bed, Beth?"

I jumped back into bed before answering. "No ma'm. I'm right here. Right here in bed."

I kept my eyes open, waiting for the doctor to come, but after a while my eyelids came together. Sleep stood by waiting for me to fall . . . fall asleep . . . sleep . . . sleep.

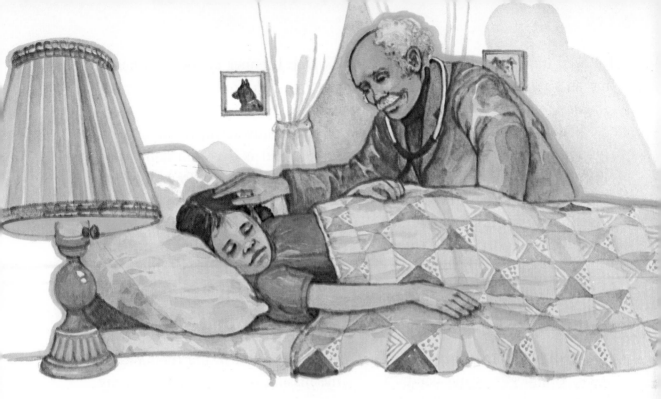

"Let me take a look at my old friend, Beth," said a big voice.

My cheeks were being patted. "Doctor's here, Beth honey," Ma was saying.

I pulled myself up to sitting and looked into the face of Dr. Brenner, who said, "This won't hurt," as he placed a stethoscope to my chest.

"Just breathe naturally," he said. He listened quietly without saying a word. Then he took the stethoscope from his ears. "I heard some wheezing sounds coming from your chest. Tell me, how do your eyes feel?"

"They feel like I want to grab them out of their sockets and give them a good scratching. They're so . . . so itchy."

"Uh-hun," answered Dr. Brenner, as though he knew all about itchy eyes. "Beth, can you remember when all this sneezing and wheezing began?"

"Yes, sir," I told the doctor. "It all started when I met Friendly."

Friendly must have heard his name called 'cause he jumped out of his carton and jogged floppily on over.

"Hi, little Friendly, little dog."

I picked him up and gave him a hug and a kiss. *"AHHHHhh-choo! Ah-choo!"*

"Beth," said Dr. Brenner, running his fingers through his silver hair. "I'm sorry to do this, but I'm going to have to tell you something. Something you're not going to like hearing. I believe you have an allergy to Friendly."

"Oh, no sir, I don't!" I cried. "I don't have one, honest. I never asked for no allergy. Why, I don't even know what that means."

Dr. Brenner took my hand. "It simply means that Friendly's dog hair is making you sick. And, furthermore, it means that he must be returned to wherever he came from."

"But Friendly is *my* dog. He belongs to me. And he's never *never* going to go back to that kennel!" I felt tears filling up my eyes. "I love Friendly. Friendly loves me."

"I know you love each other," agreed Dr. Brenner. "But all this sneezing, wheezing, and red eyes is your body's way of telling you something."

I shook my head no.

Doc Brenner nodded his head yes. "Bodies don't need to say fancy words like allergic rhinitis[1]— or any words at all, Beth. When your throat is dry, you don't wait to hear the word *water* before taking a drink. And do you really need the school's lunch bell to ring before you know when it's time to eat? Well, now your body is saying something just as important. Listen to it!" he said, cupping his hand around his ear. But the only sound in the room was the hissing noise coming from my own chest.

When the morning sun came flooding through my bedroom window, my eyes opened and I remembered about the allergy. Was it real or only a dream?

"Friendly," I called. "Come here, little Friendly."

But Friendly didn't come and I didn't hear him either. I jumped to the foot of my bed. The cardboard box was empty. They've

---

1. **allergic rhinitis** (uh•LUHR•jik ry•NY•tis): a sensitivity to something that causes sneezing and a painful, red swelling inside the nose.

taken him back to Mr. Grant's kennel!

I was just about to shout out for Friendly when outside the kitchen window I heard my brother Luther's and my sister Anne's voices: "Get that ball, Friendly. Friendly, you going to get that ball?"

Ma laughed. "That dog ain't fixing to do nothing he ain't a mind to do."

I went out the kitchen door still wearing my orange night-gown and sat down on the back steps next to her. She put her arm around me and gave me a quick squeeze. "How you feeling, honey babe?"

I thought about her question. My chest felt as though it was still filled up with old swamp water while my head carried around last night's headache. Finally, I gave my answer, "I'm OK, Mama. I reckon."

"After you come home from school, I want you to take a little nap. Never mind them chores. Just put your head down on the pillow and nap. 'Cause you spent half the night crying into your pillow."

"About what the doctor said... about taking Friendly back to the kennel. We're not going to listen to that, are we?"

She looked past me, out to where Luther and Anne were playing with Friendly. "Life don't always be the way we want it to be. Life be the way it is. Ain't nothing we can do."

"You *can't* take him back!" I shouted. "Besides, Mr. Grant probably's eaten up all the turkeys."

"If he did, he did," answered Ma.

"You don't understand," I said, bringing my voice back down to size. "I *need* Friendly! Luther was three and Anne was two when I was born so they had me, but I never had nothing little and soft to—"

"And I told you," she said, "that life be the way it be. Ain't nothing we can do. But if you misses that school bus, there is something I can do. I can take a switch to you. So *get!*"

At school I felt better and worse. Better because I didn't sneeze or wheeze and even my eyes stopped itching and watering. And worse because tonight, after supper, Friendly was going back to Mr. Grant's kennel.

If only I had some magic. One time I remembered my teacher, Miss Johnson, pointing to shelves of books and saying that they held many secrets. Could one of her books hold the secret of making the allergy go and the dog stay?

At recess, she stood on a three-step ladder to bring down a heavy book from the top shelf.

"This book may have the secret we're looking for," she said, pointing to a page. "Right here," she whispered, the way people do when they're telling secrets. "It says that people who have an allergy to long-haired dogs, like the collie, might not have an allergy to a short-haired dog, like the chihuahua."

At the kennel I held Friendly close to me while Pa explained about the allergy to Mr. Grant. "You are welcome to swap," he said, reaching out for Friendly.

"Wait!" I said. "A person has got to say good-bye, don't they?" I looked into Friendly's eyes and wondered how I could make him understand. "I never wanted to get rid of you, Friendly. I only wanted to get rid of the aller— *Her-her-choo!*—of the allergy."

He licked my ear almost as if to tell me not to worry because any dog as friendly as Friendly would get along just fine.

Again Mr. Grant reached out, only this time I gave him my Friendly. As he took him away, I heard him say, "Rest of the collies going to be mighty happy to see you again."

When he returned, Friendly wasn't with him. "An allergy sure is a bothersome thing," said Mr. Grant. "Reason I know that is because I've had an allergy ever since I was about your age."

It was so hard to believe. "You got yourself an allergy to collies too?" I asked.

"Nope." Mr. Grant pointed to the bend in his suntanned arm. "Tomatoes—that's what gets my allergy going. One tomato and my arm breaks out like a strawberry patch."

"Tomatoes don't bother me a bit," I said proudly.

"Reckon that's what an allergy is," said Mr. Grant. "It's what don't bother some folks, bothers other folks a whole lot."

When we stopped in front of the chihuahua's run, a tiny fellow came rushing to the gate, barking. "That's the dog for me," I said.

On the drive back home I held the chihuahua in my lap while my folks went back to trying to pick out a baby name. I was hoping they'd find a better name for the baby than they found for me.

When Pa turned off the high-way onto the dirt road leading to our farm, the puppy jumped off my lap. He stood on his toes, pressing his nose against the truck's window. I hollered, "Looky there! Look at Tippietoes!"

"Ohhhh," said Ma, turning her head. "Now ain't that something?

And what a fine name for him too."

I put my hands against the little dog's cheeks and gave him a kiss between the eyes. "I now name you—*ah-ah*—I now name you—*ah-ah-ah-choo!*"

"Oh, *no!*" said Ma and Pa at exactly the same time.

But finally I was able to say, and say proudly, "I now name you Tippietoes."

By the time I crawled into bed, my eyes were red and itchy. My nose was sneezy and my chest was wheezy. Ma stood at my doorway. "Tippietoes going to sleep next to the cookstove tonight, but tomorrow evening we're going to take him back."

I shook my head no. "Mama, don't say that. I don't care nothing about no little allergy. Cross my heart I don't. All I care about is my little dog. My own little Tippietoes."

"Girl, you ain't talking nothing but a heap of foolishness. I ain't about to let you walk around sick. Not as long as I'm your mama, 'cause I ain't that kind of mama. Now you get yourself to sleep."

⟶≫✦≪⟵

At first recess, I told Miss Johnson about having an allergy, not just to long-haired dogs but to short-haired ones too.

"Maybe I can find still another secret in that book," she said, bringing down the big book again. She fingered through a lot of pages before she finally began to read aloud: "People who have an allergy to both long-haired and short-haired dogs might not have an allergy to poodles, as they are the only dogs that never shed hair."

Pa explained to Mr. Grant what I had learned from the book. "So we'll be much obliged if you'll kindly swap Tippietoes here for one of your poodles."

"Fine with me," said Mr. Grant, reaching for Tippietoes.

"*Wait!*" I said, holding onto the little one for another moment. "A person still has to say good-bye." I patted his chin. He licked my fingers. "Good-bye, little boy, little Tippietoes. I'm sorry you couldn't be my dog."

I closed my eyes as I gave him over to Mr. Grant, who took him away. When he came back he said, "Come along, folks. Let me introduce you to my poodles."

We followed him until he stopped at the gate of a chain-link fence. "Poodles may be just the right dog for a girl with an allergy," he said, pointing to two white dogs that looked more like fluffy powder puffs than real dogs. "Because they never have dandruff or a doggy odor. And the book is right. They never shed a single hair."

He unhooked the gate and I walked in saying, "This time I'm going to be lucky. This time I *hope* I'm going to be lucky."

"Hope so," said Ma and Pa at exactly the same moment.

Both poodles walked over to say hello. They were quite polite. I bent down and one of the puppies came closer. "Is it you?" I asked him.

He took one step closer, resting his fluffy little head in my hand. I whispered, "I'm going to take real good care of you."

Inside the crowded cab of the pickup truck, I held the poodle puppy on my lap as Pa turned on the headlights and started for home. My patting must have relaxed the little dog 'cause he closed his eyes and went to sleep.

After a while Ma said, "I think we ought to name the baby after my great-aunt Alberta."

Pa's nose crinkled. "What you want to name our baby after her for?"

Ma's nose climbed. "Ain't she my grandma's sister? The oldest

living member of my family?"

"That nosy old lady!" said Pa.

"Aunt Alberta ain't one bit nosy," Ma corrected. "What she is, is interested. I'm disappointed in you, Mr. Eugene Lam—"

"Have you all noticed," I asked, hoping that my interruption would stop an argument from starting, "that I haven't sneezed even one time?"

Ma smiled. "Ain't it the truth."

"And Puffy will never have to go back to Mr. Grant's," I said.

"Puffy?" asked Pa, surprised.

"Don't you see," I asked, "how he's all puffy like cotton candy?"

Ma turned to look at Pa. "Beth has thought up three good names for three dogs while we is still fussing over one name for one baby."

Puffy opened his eyes and looked around. "You're here, Puffy," I said, putting my face into his white fluffiness. "And you're always going to be . . . my . . . my—*choo*! My—*ahhhhhhh-ey*!"

"Don't go telling me I heard what I think I heard," said Ma, fixing her eyes on the ceiling of the truck.

302

"It ain't what you think," I said quickly. "I really—*ahhh-choo! Ah-choo-who!* I really think I'm catching Billy Boy Williams's cold. He had one at school today. Sneezed all over the place—choo, choo, choo, like that! Spreading his germs about."

Pa drove the truck over to the side of the road and turned off the engine. "Beth, I is sorry to disappoint you. I know how much you wanted a pup, but there ain't nothing I can do."

"If you take him back," I warned, "I ain't never going to live home again. For the rest of my life I'm going to live in the kennel with Puffy."

My mama patted my hand. "In this life you got to be happy about the good things and brave about the bad ones."

"I don't want to be brave," I shouted. "All I want is my little dog."

Pa started up the truck, made a U-turn on the highway, and headed back toward the kennel. "Ain't nothing in this wide world we can do," he said, shaking his head.

The next morning I asked Miss Johnson to bring down the book again. But after a while we stopped reading. It didn't have any more secrets to tell. I walked away 'cause I didn't have a single word for a single solitary soul. But later in the afternoon I told her, "I guess it's nobody's fault. But I reckon I'm learning to be brave about things I don't like."

"And I want you to know," said Miss Johnson, taking off her glasses, "that I think you're learning very well."

When the school bus stopped in front of our sign, I jumped off and with a running leap crossed the ditch.

"How come you shortcutting through the field again?" called Philip Hall. "Ain't no dog waiting for you today."

"Guess I know that," I said, wondering how I could have forgotten. And yet for some reason I really was in a hurry to get home.

When I reached the rise, I could see the outline of my mother. But it didn't look like her, not exactly. After I passed the vegetable garden, I could see that it wasn't her. It was . . . my grandmother.

I started running my fast run. "Grandma, Grandma! Hello!"

"Howdy there, Beth babe," she called back.

I ran into her arms as she closed them around me. "How come you're here? All the way from Walnut Ridge?"

Grandma smiled. "I came to see my new grandbaby. Born this very morning, a few minutes after nine."

"Where are they?" I asked.

"Shhhhh," she said, pointing to the inside of the house. "They are both real fine, but they're resting just now."

I asked, "Is it a . . . is it a brother?"

"A brother for you, a grandson for me," she said, hugging me some more.

I danced a circle around her. "My own little brother. He's going to be fun to take care of and fun to play with. Sometimes boys are almost as much fun to play with as girls. I've noticed that."

"Reckon I've noticed that too," said Grandma, joining my dance.

"What's my brother's name?"

Grandma stopped dancing. "Your folks ain't come to no decision on that," she said.

"Don't fret about that," I told her. "I happen to be good at names."

Then I heard Pa calling from inside the house, "Beth, come on in and meet up with your brother."

I closed the screen door quietly behind me the way I always remember to do when there is a visitor in the house. Pa stood at the door of his and Ma's bedroom and waved me on. "I want you to see something real pretty," he said.

Ma was sitting up in bed, propped up by two pillows. As I came closer, I saw something in her arms that I had never seen there before. A baby.

Ma said, "Fold your arms."

"Like this?" I asked.

"Just like that," she said, placing my soft little brother in my arms.

"Ohhhhh," I said, touching my lips to his warm head. "You are a beautiful baby brother. Baby brother Benjamin."

"Benjamin?" asked Ma. "Benjamin? *Benjamin!*—Oh, yes. That's it. That's the name!"

Pa smiled. "Benjamin is a good strong name for a boy."

"Finally," said Grandma, coming into the room. "A name for the baby."

I put my face next to Baby Benjamin's and breathed in deep. I didn't sneeze. "You're always going to be our Baby Benjamin," I whispered in his ear. "And anyway, Mr. Grant wouldn't know what to do with a real baby."

Think about the story. Finish the chart on page 289.
Then answer the questions.

1. Why has Beth's family been so busy lately? How
   does this make Beth feel?

2. Why does Beth claim that she *needs* a dog?

3. Use your chart. How does Beth try to solve the
   problem with her family? What new problem does
   her solution bring?

4. How does Miss Johnson try to help Beth solve her
   problem? Is she successful? Tell why you think as
   you do.

5. Think about Beth's allergy to dogs. What other pet
   would you suggest to keep Beth from being
   lonely?

6. The selections in this unit are about people getting
   along with animals. Think about how Beth gets
   along with the three dogs. Would Beth make a
   good pet owner? Tell why you think as you do.

7. What finally happens to make Beth feel less
   lonely? Is Beth's loneliness over? Tell why you
   think as you do.

**Think
and
Discuss**

WORK IN A GROUP

Talk about things a family can do to keep family members from feeling lonely. Ask questions about what your classmates say. Talk about the answers.

Iris

Lily

Focusing on "The Black Fox"

▶ Think about a time you were in a new place. Talk about what you did to feel comfortable. Ask questions about what your classmates say.

▶ Look at the picture on pages 310–311 and read the title on page 311. Think about being in a new place.
  ● What is the setting for this story?
  ● How might you feel if you were the boy in the picture?

▶ Get ready to read about a city boy who has moved to a farm for the summer. As you read, think about how Tom changes. Think about what happens to change his feelings about life in the country. Think about what you would add to this chart.

What Happens to Tom	How Tom Feels

Now turn the page and read "The Black Fox." Then you will talk about how people change their ideas.

The Black Fox

From the story *The Midnight Fox* by Betsy Byars
Illustrated by Ron Himler

When Tom's parents leave on a two-month trip to Europe, he reluctantly goes to stay on his Aunt Millie's farm. Used to the city, Tom would rather stay there to work on his models and to be with his friend Petie Burkis.

The first three days on the farm were the longest, slowest days of my life. It seemed to me in those days that nothing was moving at all, not air, not time. Even the bees, the biggest fattest bees that I had ever seen, just seemed to hang in the air. The problem, or one of them, was that I was not an enormously adaptable person and I did not fit into new situations well.

I did a lot of just standing around those first days. I would be standing in the kitchen and Aunt Millie would turn around, stirring something, and bump into me and say, "Oh, my goodness! You gave me a scare. I didn't even hear you come in. When *did* you come in?"

"Just a minute ago."

"Well, I didn't hear you. You were so *quiet*."

Or Uncle Fred would come out of the barn wiping his hands on a rag and there I'd be, just standing, and he'd say, "Well, boy, how's it going?"

"Fine, Uncle Fred."

"Good! Good! Don't get in any mischief now."

"I won't."

I spent a lot of time at the pond and walking down the road and back. I spent about an hour one afternoon hitting the end of an old rope swing that was hanging from a tree in the front yard. I made my two models, and then I took some spare plastic strips and rigged up a harness, so that the horse was pulling the car, and Aunt Millie got very excited over this bit of real nothing and said it was the cleverest thing she had ever seen.

I wrote a long letter to Petie. I went down to the stream and made boats of twigs and leaves and watched them float out of sight. I looked through about a hundred farm magazines. I weeded Aunt Millie's flowers while she stood over me saying, "Not that, not *that*, that's a zinnia. Get the chickweed—see? Right here." And she would snatch it up for me. I had none of the difficult chores that I had expected, because the farm was so well run that everything was already planned without me. In all my life I have never spent longer, more miserable days, and I had to keep saying, "I'm fine, just fine," because people were asking me how I was all the time.

The one highlight of my day was to go down to the mailbox for the mail. This was the only thing I did all day that was of any use. Then, too, the honking of the mail truck would give me the feeling that there was a letter of great importance waiting for me in the box. I could hardly hurry down the road fast enough. Anyone watching me from behind would probably have seen only a cloud of dust, my feet would pound so fast. So far, the only mail I had received was a post card from my mom with a picture of the Statue of Liberty on it telling me how excited and happy she was.

This Thursday morning when I went to the mailbox there was a letter to me from Petie Burkis and I was never so glad to see anything in my life. I ripped it open and completely destroyed the envelope I was in such a hurry. And I thought that when I was a hundred years old, sitting in a chair with a rug over my knees, and my mail was brought in on a silver tray, I would snatch it up and rip it open just like this. I could hardly get it unfolded—Petie folds his letters up small—I was so excited.

Dear Tom,

There is nothing much happening here. I went to the playground Saturday after you left, and you know that steep bank by the swings? Well, I fell all the way down that. Here's the story—

BOY FALLS DOWN BANK WHILE GIRL
ONLOOKERS CHEER

Today Petie Burkis fell down the bank at Harley Playground. It is reported that some ill-mannered girls at the park for a picnic cheered and laughed at the sight of the young, demolished boy. The brave youngster left the park unaided.

Not much else happened. Do you get Chiller Theater? There was a real good movie on Saturday night about mushroom men.

Write me a letter,
Petie Burkis

I went in and gave the rest of the mail to Aunt Millie, who said, "Well, let's see what the government's sending us today," and then I got my box of stationery and went outside.

There was a very nice place over the hill by the creek. There were trees so big I couldn't get my arms around them, and soft grass and rocks to sit on. They were planning to let the cows into this field later on, and then it wouldn't be as nice, but now it was the best place on the farm. . . .

Anyway, I sat down and wrote Petie a letter.

Dear Petie,

I do not know whether we get Chiller Theater or not. Since there is no TV set here, it is very difficult to know what we could get if we had one.

My farm chores are feeding the pigs, feeding the chickens, weeding the flowers, getting the mail, things like that. I have a lot of time to myself and I am planning a movie about a planet that collides with Earth, and this planet and Earth become fused together, and the people of Earth are terrified of the planet, because it is very weird-looking and they have heard these terrible moanlike cries coming from the depths of it. That's all so far.

Write me a letter,
Tom

I had just finished writing this letter and was waiting for a minute to see if I could think of anything to add when I looked up and saw the black fox.

I did not believe it for a minute. It was like my eyes
were playing a trick or something, because I was just
sort of staring across this field, thinking about my
letter, and then in the distance, where the grass was
very green, I saw a fox leaping over the crest of the
field. The grass moved and the fox sprang toward the
movement, and then, seeing that it was just the wind
that had caused the grass to move, she ran straight for
the grove of trees where I was sitting.

It was so great that I wanted it to start over again,
like you can turn movie film back and see yourself
repeat some fine thing you have done, and I wanted to
see the fox leaping over the grass again. In all my life I
have never been so excited.

I did not move at all, but I could hear the paper in
my hand shaking, and my heart seemed to have
moved up in my body and got stuck in my throat.

The fox came straight toward the grove of trees.
She wasn't afraid, and I knew she had not seen me
against the tree. I stayed absolutely still even though I
felt like jumping up and screaming, "Aunt Millie! Uncle
Fred! Come see this. It's a fox, a *fox*!"

Her steps as she crossed the field were lighter and
quicker than a cat's. As she came closer I could see
that her black fur was tipped with white. It was as if it
were midnight and the moon were shining on her fur,
frosting it. The wind parted her fur as it changed
directions. Suddenly she stopped. She was ten feet
away now, and with the changing of the wind she had
got my scent. She looked right at me.

I did not move for a moment and neither did she. Her
head was cocked to one side, her tail curled up, her
front left foot was raised. In all my life I never saw anything like that fox standing there with her pale golden eyes
on me and this great black fur being blown by the wind.

Suddenly her nose quivered. It was such a slight movement I almost didn't see it, and then her mouth opened and I could see the pink tip of her tongue. She turned. She was still not afraid, but with a bound that was lighter than the wind—it was as if she was being blown away over the field—she was gone.

Still I didn't move. I couldn't. I couldn't believe that I had really seen the fox.

I had seen foxes before in zoos, but I was always in such a great hurry to get on to the good stuff that I was saying stupid things like, "I want to see the go-rilllllas," and not once had I ever really looked at a fox. Still, I could never remember seeing a black fox, not even in a zoo.

Also, there was a great deal of difference between seeing an animal in the zoo in front of painted fake rocks and trees and seeing one natural and free in the woods. It was like seeing a kite on the floor and then, later, seeing one up in the sky where it was supposed to be, pulling at the wind.

I started to pick up my pencil and write as quickly as I could, "P.S. Today I saw a black fox." But I didn't. This was the most exciting thing that had happened to me, and "P.S. Today I saw a black fox" made it nothing. "So what else is happening?" Petie Burkis would probably write back. I folded my letter, put it in an envelope, and sat there.

I thought about this old newspaper that my dad had had in his desk drawer for years. It was orange and the headline was just one word, very big, the letters about twelve inches high. WAR! And I mean it was awesome to see that word like that, because you knew it was a word that was going to change your whole life, the whole world even. And every time I would see that newspaper, even though I wasn't even born when it was printed, I couldn't say anything for a minute or two.

Well, this was the way I felt right then about the black fox. I thought about a newspaper with just one word for a headline, very big, very black letters, twelve inches high. FOX! And even that did not show how awesome it had really been to me. . . .

The days and weeks passed quickly, long warm days in which I walked through the woods looking for the black fox.

The next time I saw her was in the late afternoon at the ravine.

This was my favorite place in the forest. The sides of the ravine were heavy dark boulders with mosses and ferns growing between the rocks, and at the bottom were trunks of old dead trees. The tree trunks were like statues in some old jungle temple, idols that had fallen and broken and would soon be lost in the creeping foliage. There was only an occasional patch of sunlight.

At the top of the ravine was a flat ledge that stuck out over the rocks, and I was lying there on my stomach this particular afternoon. The rock was warm because the sun had been on it since noon, and I was half asleep when suddenly I saw something move below me. It was the black fox. There was a certain lightness, a quickness that I could not miss.

She came over the rocks as easily as a cat. Her tail was very high and full, like a sail that was bearing her forward. Her fur was black as coal, and when she was in the shadows all I could see was the white tip of her tail.

As I watched, she moved with great ease over one of the fallen trees, ran up the other side of the ravine, and disappeared into the underbrush.

I stayed exactly where I was. My head was resting on my arms, and everything was so still I could hear the ticking of my watch. I wanted to sit up. I am sort of a bony person and after I have been lying on some-thing hard for a long time, I get very uncomfortable. This afternoon, however, I did not move; I had the feeling that the fox was going to come back through the ravine and I did not want to miss seeing her.

While I was waiting I watched an ant run across the ledge with an insect wing. He was running so fast with the wing that he would make a little breeze and the wing would fly out of his grasp. Then he would go back and get the wing and start running again.

Then I watched some birds on the other side of the ravine circling over the rocks, catching insects as they skimmed the air. It was a beautiful sight, and I thought as I watched them, *That* is what man had in mind when he first said, "I want to fly." And I thought about some old genius working up in a remote mountain valley actually making a little flying machine that he could strap on his back like a knapsack, and this old man would come down to a big air base and he would go out on the flight line and announce to everyone, "Folks, I have invented a flying machine." There would be a silence and then everyone would start laughing as if they would never stop, and finally the Captain would pause long enough to explain to the old man that flying machines had *already* been invented, that right over there—that big silver thing with the huge wings, *that* was a flying machine, and over there, those enormous bullet-shaped things, *those* were flying machines. "Well," the old man would say, shaking his head sadly, "I won't waste no more of your time. I'll just head on home," and he would press a button on his knapsack, and silently, easy as a bird, he would lift off the ground, and skimming the air, fly toward the hills. For a moment everyone would be too stunned to move, and then the General would cry, "Come back, come back," and everyone at the air base would run beneath the flying old man crying, "Wait, wait, come back, come back!" because that was the way every one of those men really wanted to fly, free and easy

and silent as a bird. But the old man, who was a little
hard of hearing, would not hear their cries and would
fly off into the distance and never be seen again.

Right after I stopped thinking about this, the black
fox came back. She came down the rocks the same
way she had gone up, her white-tipped tail as light as
a plume, and I remembered a black knight I saw once
in the movies who was so tall and fine and brave you
could see his black plume racing ahead of all the other
knights when there was a battle.

She had something in her mouth that looked like a
frog—it probably was, for the creek was low now and
you could always find a frog if you wanted one. She
trotted on, apparently concerned only with getting the
frog home, and yet I had the feeling that she was
missing nothing. She passed across the ravine in a
zigzag line and started up the other side.

I did not move, and yet all at once she looked up at me. She froze for a moment, her bright eyes looking at me with curiosity rather than fear, and she cocked her head to one side, listening.

I stayed perfectly still—I was getting good at this—and we looked at each other. Then she turned away and bounded up the side of the ravine, turning at the top and disappearing into the underbrush. I felt that somewhere in the shelter of the trees she had paused to see if I was going to follow. Perhaps she wanted me to follow so she could lead me back into the forest, but I stayed where I was. After a while, I got up and went back to the farm.

The next time I saw the fox, it was a marvelous accident. These don't happen very often in real life, but they do happen, and that's what this was. Like the time Petie and I were walking down the alley behind his house and there, on top of this lady's garbage, we saw a mayonnaise jar full of marbles—not just cat's-eye marbles but all different kinds, kinds I had never seen before. Petie and I turned them all out on the grass and first Petie chose one and then I chose one until they were all gone. And both of us right now, today, have every single one of those marbles.

This was an even better accident. For the past two weeks I had been practically tearing the woods apart looking for the den of the black fox. I had poked under rocks and logs and stuck sticks in rotted trees, and it was a wonder that some animal had not come storming out and just bitten my hand off.

I had found a hornet's nest like a huge gray shield in a tree. I had found a bird's nest, low in a bush, with five pale-blue eggs and no mother to hatch them. I had found seven places where chipmunks lived. I had found a brown owl who never moved from one certain limb of one certain tree. I had heard a tree, split by lightning years ago, suddenly topple and crash to the ground, and I ran and got there in time to see a disgruntled possum run down the broken tree and into the woods. But I did not find the place where the black fox lived.

Now, on this day, I did not go into the woods at all. I had gone up the creek where there was an old chimney, all that was left of somebody's cabin. I had asked Aunt Millie about it, but all she could remember was that some people named Bowden had worked on the farm a long time ago and had lived here. I poked around the old chimney for a while because I was hoping I would find something that had belonged to the Bowdens, and then I gave that up and walked around the bend.

I sat on a rock, perfectly still, for a long time and looked down into the creek. There were crayfish in the water—I could see them, sometimes partly hidden beneath a covering of sand, or I could see the tips of their claws at the edge of a rock. There were fish in the water so small I could almost see through them. They stayed right together, these fish, and they moved together too.

After a while I looked across the creek and I saw a hollow where there was a small clearing. There was an outcropping of rocks behind the clearing and an old log slanted against the rocks. Soft grass sloped down to the creek bank.

I don't know how long I sat there—I usually forgot about my watch when I was in the woods—but it was a long time. I was just sitting, not expecting anything or waiting for anything. And the black fox came through the bushes.

She set a small bird she was carrying on the ground and gave a small yapping bark, and at once, out of a hole beneath the rocks came a baby fox.

He did not look like his mother at all. He was tiny and woolly and he had a stubby nose. He tumbled out of the hole and fell on the bird as if he had not eaten in a month. I have never seen a fiercer fight in my life than the one that baby fox gave that dead bird. He shook it, pulled it, dragged it this way and that, all the while growling and looking about to see if anyone or anything was after his prize.

The black fox sat watching with an expression of
great satisfaction. Mothers in a park sometimes watch
their young children with this same fond, pleased
expression. Her eyes were golden and very bright as
she watched the tiny fox fall over the bird, rise, and
shake it.

In his frenzy he dropped the bird, picked up an older dried bird wing in its place, and ran around the clearing. Then, realizing his mistake, he returned and began to shake the bird with even greater fierceness. After a bit he made another mistake, dropping the bird by his mother's tail, and then trying to run off with that.

In the midst of all this, there was a noise. It was on the other side of the clearing, but the black fox froze. She made a faint sound, and at once the baby fox, still carrying his bird, disappeared into the den.

The black fox moved back into the underbrush and waited. I could not see her but I knew she was waiting to lead the danger, if there was any, away from her baby. After a while I heard her bark from the woods, and I got up quietly and moved back down the creek. I did not want the black fox to see me and know that I had discovered her den. My cousin Hazeline had told me that foxes will pick up their young like cats and take them away if they think someone has discovered their den. . . .

I decided I would never come back here to bother her. I knew I would be tempted, because already I wanted to see that baby fox play with his bird some more, but I would not do it. If I was to see the black fox again, it would be in the woods, or in the pasture, or in the ravine, but I was not going to come to the den ever again. I did not know that an awful thing was going to happen which would cause me to break this resolution. . . .

Think about the story. Finish the chart on page 309.
Then answer the questions.

1. Use your chart. What is Tom's problem during his
first three days on the farm?

2. Do you think Tom is trying to fit in at the beginning
of the story? Tell why or why not.

3. Why do you think mail is so important to Tom?

4. What might Tom's aunt and uncle have done to
make Tom feel better during his first few days?

5. After Tom has spent several weeks on the farm, he
says, "I usually forgot about my watch when I was
in the woods." How have Tom's feelings changed?

6. Tell how the black fox helps Tom feel happier in
the country.

7. At the end of the story, Tom says that "an awful
thing was going to happen." What might this "awful
thing" be? How might it make Tom change his
feelings about visiting the black fox's den again?

8. How does this selection fit the unit theme of
people getting along with animals?

**Think
and
Discuss**

**WORK IN
A GROUP**

Discuss how people change in new places and situations. Talk about whether making these changes is good or bad. Ask questions about what your classmates say. Talk about the answers.

Focusing on "The Lion and the Mouse"

▶ Talk about what it means to be a friend. Ask questions about what your classmates say.

▶ Read the title of the fable on page 332 and look at the picture on page 333. Think about what you know about being a friend.

- How do you think the animals in the picture feel about each other?
- What might happen to make the animals friends?

▶ Get ready to read a fable about a Lion and a Mouse. As you read, think about what the characters' words tell about them. Think about what you might add to this chart.

Character	What the Character Says	What Is Learned About the Character

Now turn the page and read "The Lion and the Mouse." Then you will talk about the moral of the fable.

The Lion and the Mouse

An Aesop fable retold by Anne Terry White
Illustrated by Masami Sam Daijogo

In the heat of the day a Lion lay asleep at the edge of a wood. He lay so still that a Mouse ran right across his nose without knowing it was a nose, and a Lion's at that.

Bang! The Lion clapped his paw to his face and felt something caught. It was furry. Lazily he opened his eyes. He lifted up one side of his huge paw just a little bit to see what was under it and was amused to find a Mouse.

"Spare me, Great King!" he heard the little creature squeak in its tiny voice. "I didn't mean to do it! Let me go, and someday I will repay you."

"That's very funny," said the Lion, and he laughed. "How can a little thing like you help me, the great King of Beasts?"

"I don't know," the Mouse replied, "but a little creature *can* sometimes help a big one."

"Well, you have made me laugh," the Lion said, "which is something I seldom do. And anyway, you would hardly make half a mouthful. So—" He raised his paw and let the Mouse go.

A few days later the Lion was caught in a hunter's net. The woods rang with his angry roaring and the little Mouse heard him.

"That is my kind Lion!" she cried. "He is in trouble!" As fast as she could, she ran toward the spot from which the roaring came, and there he was. The Lion was thrashing around so in the net that the Mouse didn't dare to come near for fear of being crushed.

"O King, be patient!" she cried. "I will gnaw through the ropes and set you free."

So the Lion lay still while the Mouse worked away with her sharp teeth. And in a short time he was able to creep out of the net.

"You see? I told you I would repay you," the Mouse said happily. "A little creature sometimes really can help a big one."

And the Lion had to admit it was true.

Little friends may prove to be great friends.

Think and Discuss

Think about the fable. Finish the chart on page 331. Then answer the questions.

1. Use your chart. What does the Mouse say that shows she is intelligent?

2. Use your chart. How can you tell the Lion has a sense of humor?

3. Why does the Lion feel that the Mouse will never be able to help him?

4. What has the Lion learned from the Mouse at the end of the fable?

5. Think of another way the Mouse might have proved to be a great friend to the Lion.

6. Read the moral again. What lesson is the writer telling people?

7. The selections in this unit are about getting along with animals. Why does this fable belong in this unit?

WORK IN A GROUP

Fables are written to teach people lessons. How might the lesson taught in this fable be useful to you? Think of some examples of times when you might need to remember this lesson. Make a list to share with your classmates.

Focusing on "How Animals Protect Themselves"

▶ Talk about what you know about wild animals that live outside. Ask questions about what your classmates say.

▶ Read the title and subtitles of the information article. Think about what you know about animals that live outside.

- What will the information article be about?
- Which sections of the article will discuss the animals you talked about?

▶ Get ready to read an information article about animals. As you read, think about the different ways animals protect themselves. Use this chart to take notes about the article.

How Animals Protect Themselves
Armor, Quills, and Spines _____
Animals in Disguise _____
Animals That Flee _____
Other Animal Weapons _____

Now turn the page and read "How Animals Protect Themselves." Then you will talk about how animals survive.

How Animals Protect Themselves

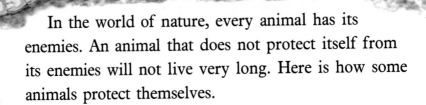

In the world of nature, every animal has its enemies. An animal that does not protect itself from its enemies will not live very long. Here is how some animals protect themselves.

Armor, Quills, and Spines

Nature has given some animals a thick coat of armor for protection. The *armadillo* is not a fighter. It does not need to be. Small plates of bone cover its body. When danger is near, the armadillo rolls itself into an armor-plated ball. Even the sharp teeth of a bobcat cannot bite through the armadillo's armor.

The *turtle* is built like an armored truck. When the turtle is scared, it pulls its head, tail, and legs into its hard shell. The common box turtle even has a shell that it closes tightly after its head, tail, and legs are safe inside.

Illustrated by Jeremy Guitar

Once a fox or weasel attacks a *porcupine,* the attacker will never try it again! When scared, the porcupine lifts its 30,000 or so quills. Each quill ends in a barb, like a fishhook. The porcupine strikes at its attacker with its quill-covered tail. It drives many quills into its attacker's face and paws. The quills keep working their way into the flesh of the enemy. If the quills pierce an important body part, the animal may die.

This *sea urchin* depends on long spines for protection. The spines of some sea urchins are poisonous.

Animals in Disguise

The *zebra* and *giraffe* have striking markings.
Yet their coloring and markings make them almost
invisible to their enemies. The zebra's stripes match
the striped pattern of sunlight and shadows in the
tall grasses where it feeds. The orange and brown
marks on the giraffe's coat resemble patches of sunshine and shadows, like those in the leaves it eats.

In the Arctic, many animals have white coats that
make it hard to see them against their snowy setting.

Some arctic foxes and hares change color with the seasons. In the summer their coats look like the gray-brown earth. In the fall the brown hairs are replaced by white ones.

The *chameleon* is also known for changing color to look like its background. The giant chameleon can change from bright yellow to blue to green in about a minute!

Animals That Flee

Many animals defend themselves by simply being fast on their feet. When danger is near, they run. As they run, they zigzag back and forth. This zigzagging helps to confuse their enemies. The table on the next page gives the top speeds of some animals that run from danger.

Animal	Top Speed
Pronghorn antelope	60 mph
Horse	47.5 mph
Jack rabbit	45 mph
White-tailed deer	40 mph
Giraffe	32 mph

Other Animal Weapons

The *skunk* has a strange weapon, but it is a most powerful one! If an enemy comes near, the skunk beats its front feet on the ground. If the attacker comes even closer, then the skunk turns around and fires its famous smell. The enemy quickly learns a lesson it will not forget!

Even a coyote is afraid to attack the *badger*. With its sharp teeth and long claws, the badger is a fierce fighter. The honey badger of Africa fears no animal. It will attack even large snakes.

Some animals' teeth can be deadly weapons. Wolves' teeth are sharp and pointed. They fit together so closely, they can cut like the blade of a knife.

Nature has given some animals horns or antlers to use as weapons. These animals use their horns or antlers to keep enemies from getting close. Some also use their horns or antlers to push or throw enemies out of the way.

In the animal kingdom, each animal has its enemies. Each animal also has ways to keep itself safe. In the battle for survival, each animal uses whatever weapons it has for staying alive.

Think about the article. Look at the notes you made as you read. Then answer the questions.

1. Use your notes. Think about what you know about wild animals. Why is protection important to animals?

2. In what way is the sea urchin's protection like the porcupine's? How is it different?

3. How does the arctic hare protect itself in winter?

4. Under which subtitle might a snail belong? Tell why you think as you do.

5. How can the size of an animal protect it?

6. The selections in this unit all are about people and animals living together. What can people do to help animals survive?

Choose *one* environment and *one* feature of an enemy from this chart. Decide what kinds of animals would survive best in this environment and against this kind of enemy. Explain your answers to classmates. Ask questions about what your classmates say.

WORK IN A GROUP

Environment	desert	ocean	jungle
Enemies Have	sharp teeth	speed	good eyesight

TALKING ABOUT THE SELECTIONS

You have read these selections.

Buying a Puppy

An Allergy Is a Bothersome Thing

The Black Fox

The Lion and the Mouse

How Animals Protect Themselves

Talk about the selections you have read. Consider how the ideas and characters are alike and different. Talk about the theme.

1. How are Beth Lambert and Tom alike? How are they different from one another?

2. How do you think the black fox protects itself against humans or other creatures that come too near?

3. How do you think Beth Lambert would feel after reading the poem "Buying a Puppy"?

4. What do the selections show about the ways in which people and animals live together?

BOOKSHELF

Hawk, I'm Your Brother by Byrd Baylor. Charles Scribner's, 1976. Rudy Soto plans to steal a baby hawk from a nest, hoping the hawk will help him learn to fly.

Reynard: The Story of a Fox Returned to the Wild by Alice Mills. Atheneum, 1986. A red fox is found on the highway. It must be taught how to survive before it can be sent back to the wild.

An Insect's Body by Joanna Cole. William Morrow, 1984. Have you ever wondered what a cricket really looks like? This book takes a close look at the common house cricket.

Ground Squirrels by Colleen S. Bare. Dodd, Mead, 1980. The California ground squirrel and others have many habits that this book will help you understand.

Nature's Champions: The Biggest, the Fastest, the Best by Alvin and Virginia Silverstein. Random House, 1980. For nature lovers, this book describes more than twenty-five plants and animals that are unusual in some way.

A Swinger of Birches: Poems of Robert Frost for Young People by Robert Frost. Stemmer House, 1982. Discover and feel the beauty of nature in poetry form.

6 When Paths Cross

TALKING ABOUT THE THEME

Look at the picture on pages 348 and 349 and read the title.

1. Who are the characters in this picture? What are they doing?

2. What do you think the picture has to do with the title?

3. What are some things that can happen when people's paths cross?

4. How could crossing paths with someone change your life?

5. How do you think the selections in this unit will be alike?

Other Books About Meetings That Change Lives

A Girl Called Al by Constance C. Green. Viking, 1969. Two girls learn much from one another and from their friendship with an elderly superintendent in their apartment house.

Zeely by Virginia Hamilton. Macmillan, 1967. An encounter with a mysterious neighbor makes this young black girl take a closer look at herself.

Flat on My Face by Julia First. Camelot Books, 1975. Though she is the best player on the baseball team, Laura just wants to be popular. A new friend who has cerebral palsy helps her decide what matters most to her.

Focusing on "Mexicali Soup"

▶ Talk about how your favorite food is made. Ask questions about what your classmates say.

▶ Read the title on page 352 and look at the story pictures. Think about what you know about making your favorite food.

- What do you think is the favorite food of the family in this story?
- What things might be in Mexicali Soup?

▶ Get ready to read a story about a family's special soup. As you read, pay attention to how each character would change the things in the soup. Think about what you would add to this chart.

How to Make Mexicali Soup

Character's Name	Thing He or She Wants Left Out	Reason

Now turn the page and read "Mexicali Soup." Then you will talk about whether the old ways or new ways are better.

Mexicali Soup

A story by Kathryn Hitte and William D. Hayes
Illustrated by Bill and Judy Anderson

All the way across town Mama sang to her-
self—to herself and the little one, little Juanita. Here
on the streets of the great fine city, she sang an
old tune from the old home in the mountains. And
she thought of what she would buy in the markets.

Only the best of everything. Potatoes and peppers—the best! Tomatoes and onions—the best!
The best garlic. The best celery. And then, cooked
all together, ah! The best soup in the world!
Mama's Special Mexicali Soup. The soup that
always made everyone say, "Mama makes the
best soup in the world."

"Ah, *sí!*" Mama thought with a smile. "Yes!
Our supper tonight will be a very special supper
for my Rosie and Antonio and Juan and Manuel
and Maria, and for the little one—and for Papa,
too. A very special supper of my Mexicali Soup."

352

"Mama! Yoo-hoo, Mama!"

There was the fine new school building where Juan and Manuel and Maria went to school, and there was Maria with her new city friend, waving and calling.

"Wait a minute, Mama!" Maria came running to put her schoolbooks in the stroller with Juanita. "Mama, may I play a while at Marjorie's house? Please?"

"Very well," Mama said. "A while. But do not be late for supper, Maria. I am making my special soup tonight."

"Mmmm-mmm, Mexicali Soup!" Maria said. Then she looked thoughtful. Then she frowned. "But—Mama?"

"Yes, Maria?"

"Mama, there are such a lot of potatoes in your Mexicali Soup."

"Of course," Mama said, smiling.

"Marjorie doesn't eat potatoes. Her mother doesn't eat them. Her sister doesn't eat them. Potatoes are too fattening, Mama. They are too fattening for many people in the city. I think we should do what others do here. We are no longer in the mountains of the West, Mama, where every-one eats potatoes. We are in the city now. So would you—Mama, would you please leave out the potatoes?"

"No potatoes," Mama said thoughtfully. She looked at Maria's anxious face. She shrugged. "Well, there are plenty of good things in the Mexicali Soup without potatoes. I will add more of everything else. It will still make good soup."

Maria kissed Mama's cheek. "Of course it will, Mama. You make the best soup in the world."

Mama went on with Juanita to the markets, to the street of little markets, thinking aloud as she went. "Tomatoes, onions, celery. Red peppers, chili peppers, good and hot. And garlic. But no potatoes."

Mama went to Mr. Santini's little market for the best tomatoes and celery. She went to Mr. Vierra's little market for the best onions and garlic. "And the peppers," she said to Juanita. "We will buy the peppers from Antonio. Our own Antonio, at the market of Mr. Fernandez. Here is the place. Ah! What beautiful peppers!"

Antonio came hurrying out of the store to the little stand on the sidewalk. "Let me help you, Mama! I hope you want something very good for our supper tonight. I get very hungry working here," Antonio said.

"Ah, *sí!*" Mama said. "Yes, Antonio. For to-night—something special!" She reached for the hot red peppers strung above her head. "Mexicali Soup."

"Hey! That's great," Antonio exclaimed. Then he looked thoughtful. Then he frowned. "But— Mama—"

"Yes?" Mama said, putting some peppers on the scale.

"Well—Mama, you use a lot of hot peppers in your soup."

"Of course," Mama said, smiling.

"A lot," Antonio repeated. "Too many, Mama. People here don't do that. They don't cook that way. They don't eat the way we did in the mountains of the West. I know, Mama. I have worked here for weeks now, after school and Saturdays. And in all that time, Mama, I have not sold as many hot peppers to other ladies as you use in a week.

"*Mamacita*," Antonio said. "Please don't put hot peppers in the soup."

"No peppers," Mama said thoughtfully. She looked at Antonio's anxious face. "Well—" Mama shrugged. "There are plenty of good things in the soup without peppers. I will add more of something else. It will still make good soup."

Antonio took the peppers out of the scale and put them back on the stand. "Of course it will, Mama." He kissed her cheek. "Everyone knows you make the best soup in the world."

Mama went on with Juanita toward home. "Tomatoes, onions, garlic, celery," she said to herself. "Yes. I can still make a good soup with those." She hummed softly to herself as she crossed a

street blocked off from traffic, a street that was only for play.

"Hey, Mama! *Mamacita*!"

Juan and Manuel left the game of stickball in the play street. They raced each other to the spot where Mama stood.

"Oh, boy! Food!" said Juan when he saw the bags in the stroller. He opened one of the bags. "Tomatoes and celery—I know what that means."

"Me, too," said Manuel. He peeked into the other bag. "Onions and garlic. Mexicali Soup! Right, Mama?" Manuel rubbed his stomach and grinned. Then he looked thoughtful. Then he frowned. "But, Mama—listen, Mama."

"I am listening," Mama said.

"Well, I think we use an awful lot of onions," Manuel said. "They don't use so many onions in the lunchroom at school, or at the Boy's Club picnics. You know, Mama, they have different ways of doing things here, different from the ways of our town on the side of the mountain. I think we should try new ways. I think we shouldn't use so many onions. *Mamacita*, please make the Mexicali Soup without onions."

"Manuel is right!" Juan said. "My teacher said only today there is nothing that cannot be changed, and there is nothing so good that it cannot be made better, if we will only try. I think there may be better ways of making soup than our old way. Make the soup tonight without tomatoes, Mama!"

"No tomatoes?" Mama said. "And no onions? In Mexicali Soup?" Mama looked at the anxious faces of Juan and Manuel. Then she shrugged. She closed the two bags of groceries carefully. She pushed the stroller away from the play street. She shrugged again.

Voices came after her. Juan's voice said, "We will be hungry for your soup tonight, Mama!" Manuel's voice called, "*Mamacita*! You make the best soup in the world!"

In the big kitchen at home, Mama put the
groceries on the table by the stove. She hummed
a little soft tune that only Mama could hear. She
stood looking at the groceries. No potatoes. No
peppers. Tomatoes—Mama pushed the tomatoes
aside. Onions—she pushed the onions aside.

Mama sat down and looked at what was left.

The front door clicked open and shut. Rosie
came into the kitchen. Rosita, the young lady of
the family.

"Hi, Mama. Oh, Mama—I hope I'm in time! I heard you were making—" Rosie stopped to catch her breath. She frowned at the groceries on the table. "All the way home I heard it. The boys and Maria—they all told me—and Mama! I want to ask you—please! No garlic."

Mama stopped humming.

Rosie turned up her nose and spread out her hands. "No garlic. Please. Listen, Mama. Last night, when my friend took me to dinner, I had such a fine soup! Delicious! The place was so elegant, Mama—so refined. So expensive. And no garlic at all in the soup!"

Rosie bent over and kissed Mama's cheek. "Just leave out the garlic, *Mamacita*. You make the best soup in the world."

362

A deep voice and many other voices called all at once, and the front door shut with a bang. "Mama! We are home, Mama!" Then all of them, Juan and Manuel and Antonio, with Maria pulling Papa by the hand—all of them came to stand in the kitchen doorway.

Papa reached for the baby, the little Juanita, and swung her onto his shoulders. "I have heard of something special," Papa said. "I have heard we are having Mexicali Soup tonight."

Mama said nothing. But Mama's eyes flashed fire. She waited.

"Your soup, Mama—" Papa said. "It is simply the best soup in the world!"

"Ah, *sí!* But you want me to leave out something?" Mama's voice rose high. "The celery, perhaps? You want me to make my Mexicali Soup without the celery?"

Papa raised his eyebrows. "Celery?" Papa opened his hands wide and shrugged. "What is celery? It is a little nothing! Put it in or leave it out, *Mamacita*—it does not matter. The soup will be just as—"

"Enough!" Mama said. "Out of my kitchen—all of you!" Mama waved her arms wide in the air. The fire in Mama's eyes flashed again. "I am busy! I am busy getting your supper. I will call you. Go."

"But, Mama," said Rosie, "we always help you with—"

"No!" Mama said. "Out!"

Rosie and Juan and Manuel, Antonio and Maria, and Papa with the baby, tiptoed away to the living room.

There was only silence coming from the kitchen. Then, the sound of a quiet humming. Soon the humming mixed with the clatter of plates and spoons, the good sounds of the table being set for supper.

The humming turned into singing. Mama was singing a happy song from the old home in the mountains. Juan and Manuel, Antonio and Maria, Rosie and Papa, looked at one another and smiled and nodded. Mama was singing.

Then from the kitchen Mama's voice called to them. "The soup is finished. Your supper is ready. Come and eat now."

"Ah! That is what I like to hear," said Papa, jumping up with Juanita. "The soup is ready before I have even begun to smell it cooking."

"Mmm-mmm!" said Juan and Manuel, racing for the big kitchen table.

"Mmm-mmm!" said Maria and Antonio and Rosie when they saw the steaming bowls on the table. "Mama makes the best soup in the world."

But what was the matter?

"This doesn't look like Mexicali Soup," said Maria, staring at the bowl before her.

"It doesn't smell like Mexicali Soup," said Antonio, sniffing the steam that rose from his bowl.

"It doesn't taste like Mexicali Soup," said Juan and Manuel, sipping a sip from their spoons.

"This is not Mexicali Soup," said Rosie, setting her spoon down hard with a clang. "This is nothing but hot water!"

Everyone looked at Mama.

Mama smiled and hummed the old tune from the mountains.

"You have forgotten to bring the soup, *Mamacita*?" suggested Papa.

"No," Mama said, still smiling. "The soup is in your bowls. And it is just what you wanted. I made the soup the way my family asked me to make it.

"I left out the potatoes that Maria does not want. I left out the peppers that Antonio does not want. I left out the tomatoes that Juan does not want. I left out the onions that Manuel does not want. For Rosita, I left out the garlic. And for Papa, I left out the celery, the little nothing that does not matter.

"The *new* Mexicali Soup! It is so simple! So quick! So easy to make," Mama said. "You just leave everything out of it."

Think about the selection. Finish the chart on page 351. Then answer the questions.

1. Use your chart. What do all the characters do that is the same? What do they say that is the same?

2. How does Mama feel at the beginning of the story? Why do her feelings change?

3. Use your chart. What are some reasons the children give Mama for leaving things out of her soup?

4. How does Mama feel about the old life in the mountains? How does she feel about the new life in the city? Give reasons for your answers.

5. How do the children feel about the new ways of the city? Tell why you think as you do.

6. The selections in this unit all are about people growing as they meet others with different ideas. How do you think this family will grow from working out the problem of Mexicali Soup?

**WORK IN
A GROUP**

Talk about why Mexicali Soup is a symbol of the old ways for Mama. Ask questions about what your classmates say. Talk about the answers.

Focusing on "The Turkey or the Eagle?"

Think and Read

▶ Think about symbols of the United States. On a sheet of paper, quickly write as much as you can about these symbols. After you have finished, share your ideas with your classmates.

▶ Read the title on page 370 and look at the pictures. Think about what you know about symbols of the United States.

- Why do you think the title is a question?
- What do you think this selection will be about?

▶ Get ready to read an information article about two kinds of birds that could be used as national symbols. As you read, think about how the birds are different. Use this chart to take notes as you read.

"The Turkey or the Eagle?"

Wild Turkey	Bald Eagle

Now turn the page and read "The Turkey or the Eagle?" Then you will talk about differences of opinion.

The Turkey or the Eagle?

I'm a true native of America.

When the United States first declared itself a free country, its leaders felt that the new nation needed a symbol. The leaders wanted a symbol that would stand for the ideals that their new country was fighting for. From July 1776 until June 1782, many ideas were suggested.

One idea was the Greek hero Hercules, who is thought to be very strong and brave. Another idea was Moses, who is said to have led the people of Israel out of Egypt and into the Promised Land. A third idea was Liberty and Justice drawn as strong women overcoming the English king, George III.

The United States Congress did not like any of these ideas. Then, in 1782, a Philadelphian named William Barton drew a picture that showed a golden eagle as the symbol of the new country. Secretary of Congress Charles Thompson changed the golden eagle to the American bald eagle.

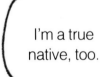

I'm a true native, too.

After making a few more changes to Mr. Barton's design, Secretary Thompson presented the design to Congress. Congress liked it. On June 20, 1782, the American bald eagle became the official symbol of the new United States of America.

Right away, many people disagreed with the choice of the bald eagle. These people thought that

Illustrated by Ed Parker

the American wild turkey would have been a more fitting choice. The argument between these two groups has continued to this very day. Read why each side believes its choice to be the right one. Then decide for yourself.

Wild Turkey

People who wanted the wild turkey pointed out that it was a true American. The bird had always been admired by the Indians. When colonists came to the eastern shores, the wild turkey quickly became a favorite. The colonists thought that it was one of the most beautiful birds in the New World. The wild turkey's bronze-green feathers were prized as decorations for the colonists' hats or blankets.

People also thought that the wild turkey was a proud bird. Its great size and weight seemed to give it a stately appearance. A full-grown wild turkey weighs between ten and thirty pounds. It is four feet long from the tip of its beak to its tail feathers and stands three feet tall. The bird's broad wings can open to a length of five feet from one wing tip to the other.

Wild turkeys are also known for their swiftness and sharp senses. Wild turkeys do not fly very often, but they *do* run—up to 20 miles an hour. They also have very sharp eyesight and hearing. Hunters say that a wild turkey can easily lead them into wild forest country and then get away.

Ben Franklin summed up the argument for the wild turkey by pointing out that it was not only a handsome and useful bird, but also a "respectable" one. The wild turkey gathers its own food supply of small nuts, seeds, and insects. The bald eagle has been known to take prey caught by another bird.

Bald Eagle

Many people agreed with the choice of the bald eagle as the symbol of the United States. They said that it, too, was a true American, for the bald eagle can be found only in North America. With its shining white head feathers and its deep brown wings, it is considered by many people to be a very handsome bird.

An American bald eagle stands three feet tall from beak tip to *talons,* or claws. Those same talons and hooked beak, along with the bird's large pale eyes, make the American bald eagle look fierce and brave. With outspread wings, the American bald eagle measures seven feet long and seems to fly effortlessly. Many people say that the bald eagle flies so high that it disappears from sight.

Those people who favor the eagle point out that it feeds mostly on fish and other small animals. They say that the eagle takes prey from other birds only when the food supplies are short. President Kennedy said this about the bald eagle: "The fierce beauty and proud independence of this great bird aptly symbolize the strength and freedom of America."

Think about the information article. Look at the notes you made as you read. Then answer the questions.

1. Use your notes. Why did leaders of the United States first decide to look for a national symbol?

2. Use your notes. What things about wild turkeys and bald eagles does the writer compare? How does this help readers form their own opinions?

3. Think about the state in which you live. Name an animal that could be your state's symbol. Tell why you think as you do.

4. What are some words the writer uses to show that there were different opinions about a good national symbol?

5. This selection shows an example of people in government having differences of opinion. Is it good to have differences of opinion in government? Tell why you think as you do.

6. The selections in this unit all are about people growing by working out differences. How does our country grow by working out differences?

WORK IN A GROUP

Talk about working out differences of opinion. Discuss how our government works out differences of opinion. Discuss how you work out differences of opinion with others. Ask questions about what your classmates say. Talk about the answers.

Focusing on "The Monkey and the Crocodile"

Think and Read

▶ Talk about people you know who are smart. Ask questions about what your classmates say.

▶ Read the title and introduction on page 376. Think about what you know about people who are smart.
  ● Which animal is smarter—the Monkey or the Crocodile? Tell why you think as you do.
  ● What do you think might happen in the story?

▶ Get ready to read about what happens to the Monkey and the Crocodile. As you read, think about what each animal does because of the other. Think about what you would add to this drawing.

What the Monkey Does   What the Crocodile Does

Now turn the page and read "The Monkey and the Crocodile." Then you will talk about matching strength against brains.

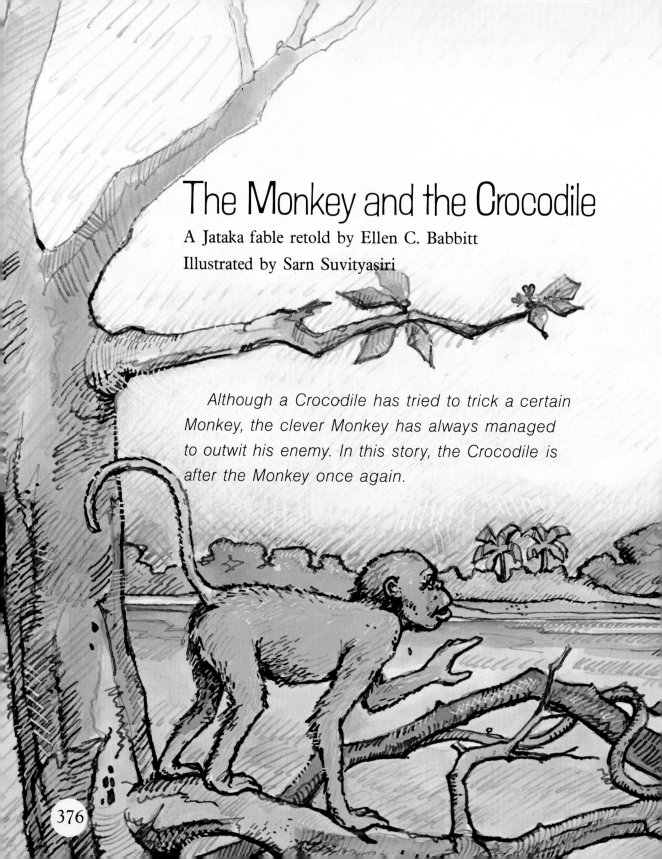

The Monkey and the Crocodile

A Jataka fable retold by Ellen C. Babbitt

Illustrated by Sarn Suvityasiri

Although a Crocodile has tried to trick a certain Monkey, the clever Monkey has always managed to outwit his enemy. In this story, the Crocodile is after the Monkey once again.

The Monkey lived in a great tree on a river-bank. The Monkey soon moved away from that tree. He wanted to get away from the Crocodile, so that he might live in peace.

But the Crocodile found him, far down the river, living in another tree.

In the middle of the river was an island covered with fruit trees. Halfway between the bank of the river and the island, a large rock rose out of the water. The Monkey could jump to the rock, and then to the island. The Crocodile watched the Monkey crossing from the bank of the river to the rock, and then to the island.

He thought to himself, "The Monkey will stay on the island all day, and I'll catch him on his way home at night."

The Monkey had a fine feast, while the Crocodile swam about, watching him all day.

Toward night the Crocodile crawled out of the water and lay on the rock, perfectly still.

When it grew dark among the trees, the Monkey started for home. He ran down to the river bank, and there he stopped.

"What is the matter with the rock?" the Monkey thought to himself. "I never saw it so high before. The Crocodile is lying on it!"

But he went to the edge of the water and called, "Hello, Rock!"

No answer.

Then he called again, "Hello, Rock!"

Three times the Monkey called, and then he said, "Why is it, Friend Rock, that you do not answer me tonight?"

"Oh," said the stupid Crocodile to himself. "The rock answers the Monkey at night. I'll have to answer for the rock this time."

So he answered: "Yes, Monkey! What is it?"

The Monkey laughed, and said, "Oh, it's you, Crocodile, is it?"

"Yes," said the Crocodile. "I am waiting here for you. I am going to eat you."

"You have caught me in a trap this time," said the Monkey. "There is no other way for me to go home. Open your mouth wide so I can jump right into it."

Now the Monkey well knew that, when Crocodiles open their mouths wide, they shut their eyes.

While the Crocodile lay on the rock with his mouth wide open and his eyes shut, the Monkey jumped.

But not into his mouth! Oh, no! He landed on the top of the Crocodile's head, and then sprang quickly to the bank. Up he whisked into his tree.

When the Crocodile saw the trick the Monkey had played on him, he said, "Monkey, you have great cunning. You know no fear. I'll let you alone after this."

"Thank you, Crocodile," said the Monkey. "But I shall be on the watch for you just the same."

Think about the selection. Finish the drawing on page 375. Then answer the questions.

1. Use your drawing. What is the Monkey's plan? What is the Crocodile's plan?

2. Why do you think the Crocodile is so eager to catch the Monkey?

3. Use your drawing. The Crocodile pretends to be part of the rock. How does the Monkey fool him into talking?

4. Think about what the Crocodile says at the end of the fable. Do you think he is telling the truth? Tell why you think as you do.

5. This story is in a unit about how people learn from meeting someone with different ideas. Who learns something in this selection? What does he learn?

6. What words would you use to describe what the Monkey is like? What words would you use to describe what the Crocodile is like?

7. Name other animals the writer might have used instead of the Monkey and the Crocodile. Tell why you think as you do.

WORK IN A GROUP

Think about the fable. What do you think the moral of this animal fable is? What lesson about *people* does the writer of this fable want to teach the readers? Ask questions about what your classmates say. Talk about the answers.

Focusing on "Sound of Sunshine, Sound of Rain"

▶ What kinds of sounds are there? What can sounds tell you? On a sheet of paper, quickly write as much as you can about sounds. After you have finished writing, share your ideas with your classmates.

▶ Look at the picture on page 384. Read the title. Think about what you know about sounds.

● What sound does rain have? What sound does sunshine have?

● What do you think this story might be about?

▶ Get ready to read about why sounds are important to the boy in the picture. As you read, think about how this boy sees the things and people around him. Think about what you would add to this chart.

What the Boy Hears	What the Boy Touches	What the Boy Learns

Now turn the page and read "Sound of Sunshine, Sound of Rain." Then you will talk about how people can see places differently.

Sound of Sunshine, Sound of Rain

A story by Florence Parry Heide
Illustrated by Kenneth Longtemps

Morning Voices

It must be morning, for I hear the morning
voices.

I have been dreaming of a sound that whispers
Follow me, Follow me, but not in words. I follow the
sound up and up until I feel I am floating in the air.

Now I am awake, and I listen to the voices.

My mother's voice is warm and soft as a pillow.

My sister's voice is little and sharp and high, like
needles flying in the air.

I do not listen to the words but to the sound. Low, high, low, high, soft, hard, soft, hard, and then the sounds coming together at the same time and making a new sound. And with it all, the sharp sounds of my sister's heels putting holes in what I hear.

Then I hear the slamming of kitchen drawers and the banging of pans and there is no more talking.

My bed is in the living room. I reach out to feel whether my mother has laid my clothes on the chair beside my bed. They are there, and I feel the smoothness and the roughness of them.

I reach under the chair to find which shoes my mother has put there. They are my outside shoes, not my slippers, so today must be a warm day. Maybe I can go to the park.

I tap my good luck song on the wall beside my bed.

I put my feet on the floor and feel the cool wood and curl my toes against it. Then it is four steps to the table, then around the table, touching the chairs, and then seven steps to the window. I put my cheek against the window, and I can feel the warm sun. Now I am sure I can go to the park, if my sister has time to take me on her way to study.

I take my clothes into the bathroom, and I wash and dress there. Hot water, cold water, soapy water, plain water, loud water, still water. Then I make sure I have turned the faucets tight. I make sure I have buttoned all of my buttons the right way, or my sister will be cross, and maybe not have time to take me to the park.

I tap my good luck song against the door before I open it.

When I open the door, I hear the voices again. My sister's voice is like scissors cutting away at my mother's voice.

I sit at the table, and my mother gives me my breakfast. I breathe on the hot chocolate so I can feel it on my face coming back warm. I drink just a little at a time so I can keep holding the warm cup.

"Eat while it's hot," says my sister to me, loudly.

"Does he have to be so slow?" says my sister to my mother in her quiet voice. My sister thinks because I cannot see that maybe I cannot hear very well, and she talks loudly to me, and softly when she does not want me to hear, but I hear.

"You spilled," says my sister, loudly.

"I can't be late," she says in her quiet voice to my mother. "Everybody's always late but me, and I won't be late."

After breakfast I go over to the window again. When I put my cheek against the glass it is warmer than before, so today will be a good day. I tap my good luck song against the window.

My sister says she will take me to the park on her way to study. She gives me my jacket and tells me to wait for her outside on the steps.

I go down the outside steps. There are seven steps. Seven is my most magic number. Seven up, seven down, seven up, seven down. I go up and down, waiting for my sister.

My sister comes out. She takes my hand. She walks very fast, but I can still count the steps to the park, and I can still remember the turns. Someday I can go there by myself. I listen to the street noises and try to sort them out.

My sister's hand is not soft. I can feel her nails, little and sharp, like her voice, and I listen to her heels making holes in all the other sounds.

The park seems a long way off.

When we get to the park we go first to the bench. My sister waits to make sure I remember my way in the park. Fourteen steps to the bubbler. Around the bubbler, twenty steps to the curb.

I go back to the bench. I try to hurry so my sister won't have to wait long and be cross. Now seventeen steps to the phone booth, four benches on the way and I touch them all. Then I come back to my bench. My sister puts money in my pocket so I can telephone.

She talks to me and to herself.

"Filthy park," she says, and it is as if she were stepping on the words. "No grass. Trees in cages. Since when do benches and old newspapers make a park?" She pulls my jacket to straighten it.

Now she is gone and I have my morning in the sun.

389

I try each bench, but mine is still the best one.

I go to the bubbler and press my mouth against the water and feel it on my tongue, soft and warm. I put my finger on the place where the water comes out. I walk around and around the bubbler, and then I try to find my bench. It is one of my games. I have many games.

I walk over to the telephone booth, touching the four benches on the way. I stand inside the booth. I feel in my pocket to see if the money my sister gave me is still there. It is.

I practice dialing our number so I will be sure I have it right. Then I put my dime in and call. I let it ring two times and then I hang up and get my dime back. My sister says that way my mother will know I am all right.

I blow on the glass and it blows back to me. I tap my good luck song on it and go back to my bench.

I play one of my games. I listen to every sound and think if that sound would be able to do something to me, what it would do. Some sounds would scratch me, some would pinch me, some would push me. Some would carry me, some would crush me, and some would rock me.

A New Voice

I am sitting on my bench tapping my good luck song with my shoes when I hear the bells of an ice cream truck. I feel the money in my pocket. I have

the dime and I also have a bigger one. I know I have enough for an ice cream bar.

I walk out to the curb, touching the cages around the trees. I wait until the bells sound near, and I wave.

The ice cream man stops. He is near enough for me to touch his cart. I hold out my money.

Now I feel him seeing me, but he does not take my money.

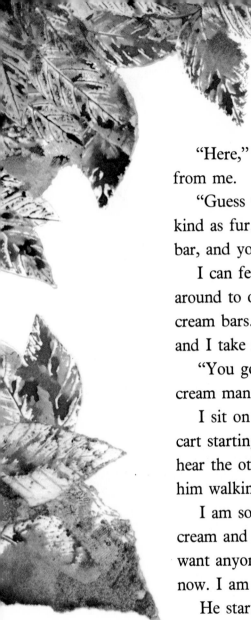

"Here," I say, but he does not take the money from me.

"Guess what?" he says, and his voice is soft and kind as fur. "Every tenth kid wins a free ice cream bar, and you're the lucky one today."

I can feel him getting off his cart and going around to open the place where he keeps his ice cream bars. I can feel him putting one near my hand and I take it. I start back to my bench.

"You gonna be okay by yourself now?" the ice cream man calls, so I know he is seeing me.

I sit on the bench. I listen for the sound of his cart starting up and his bells ringing, but I can only hear the other sounds, the regular ones. Then I hear him walking over to my bench.

I am sorry, because I only want to feel the ice cream and see how long I can make it last. I do not want anyone to sit with me, but he is sitting with me now. I am afraid I will spill and he will see me.

He starts to talk, and his voice is soft as a sweater. His name is Abram. He tells me about the park.

My sister says the trees are in cages because if they weren't in cages they wouldn't stay in such a terrible park. They'd just get up and go somewhere pretty.

Abram says the trees are in cages to keep them safe so they can grow up to be big and tall. "Like sides on a crib for a baby, keeping him from falling and hurting himself," says Abram.

My sister says the park is ugly and dirty.

Abram says there are a few little bits of paper, and a couple of cans and some bottles, but he says he can squint up his eyes and all those things lying around shine like flowers. Abram says you see what you want to see.

My sister says the park is just for poor folks, and that no one would ever come here if they had a chance to go anywhere else.

Abram says the park is just for lucky people, like him and me. He says the people who come to this park can see things inside themselves, instead of just what their eyes tell them.

After a while Abram goes away. He says he will come back and look for me tomorrow. I hear his ice cream bells go farther and farther away until I do not hear them anymore.

While I am waiting for my sister to come for me, I fall asleep on the bench. I have a good dream. I dream that Abram lifts me so I can touch the leaves of a tree. All of the leaves are songs, and they fall around me and cover me. I am warm and soft under the songs.

My sister shakes me awake. "You'll catch cold lying here," she says.

The next day while I am sitting on my bench, I hear the ice cream bells and I walk out to the curb, touching the cages of the trees as I go. Abram gives me an ice cream bar and we walk together back to the bench. I do not have to touch the cages because I am with him.

After I finish my ice cream bar, Abram gives me some paper clips so I can feel them in my pocket. He shows me how I can twist them to make little shapes.

After he leaves, I feel them. There are seven paper clips.

That night I dream that someone is gathering in a big net everything in the world that makes a sound, and I am tumbled in the net with dogs and cars and whistles and busses. I try to get out of the net and my sister shakes me awake.

"Stop thrashing around," she says. "You're all tangled up in the blanket."

Something Special

The next day Abram brings me a balloon. I can feel it round and tight. It tugs at the string.

Abram says some balloons are filled with something special that makes them want to fly away, up to the sun, and this balloon is filled with that something special.

He says some people are filled with something special that makes them pull and tug, too, trying to get up and away from where they are.

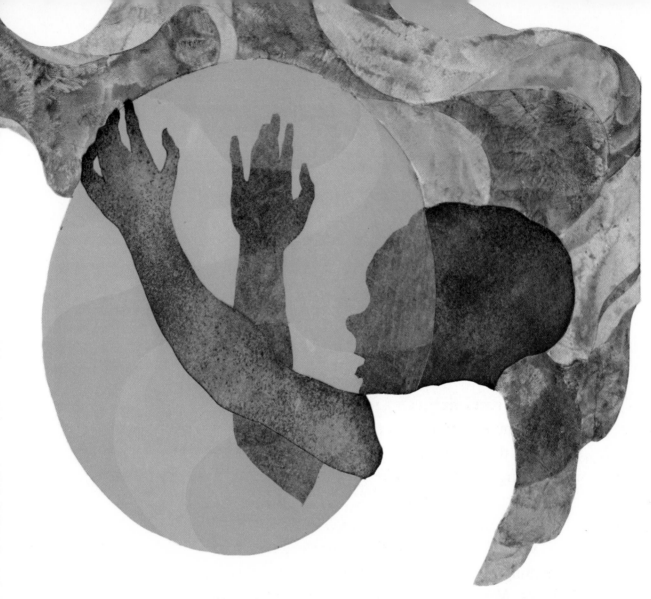

His voice is like a kitten curled on my shoulder.

He tells me my balloon is red, and then he tells me about colors.

He says colors are just like sounds. Some colors are loud, and some colors are soft, and some are big and some are little, and some are sharp and some are tender, just like sounds, just like music.

What is the best color, I wonder?

He says all colors are the same, as far as that goes. There isn't a best color, says Abram. There isn't a good color or a bad color.

Colors are just on the outside. They aren't important at all. They're just covers for things, like a blanket.

Color doesn't mean a thing, says Abram.

When my sister comes, she asks me where I got my balloon. I tell her about my friend. I hold on to the string of my balloon while we walk.

When we get home, I tie the string of my balloon to my chair.

I have a bad dream in the night. I dream that my ears are sucking in every sound in the world, so many sounds I cannot breathe. I am choking with the sounds that are pulled into me and I have to keep coughing the sounds away as they come in or I will smother.

"Here's some stuff for your cold," says my sister.

When I am awake again, I cannot tell if it is morning. I hear noises but they are not the morning noises. My sister has her quiet voice, and I do not hear the little hard sounds of her heels making holes in the morning.

She is wearing slippers. She tells my mother she is not going to go to study today.

There is no hurry about today. I reach for my balloon. The string lies on the chair, and I find the balloon on the floor, small and soft and limp. It does not float. It lies in my hand, tired and sad.

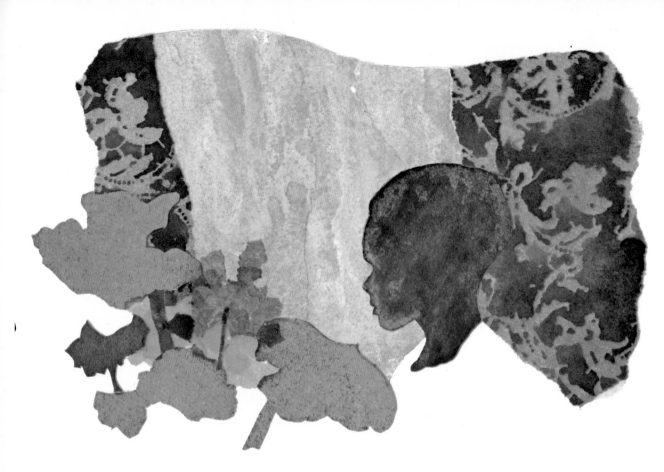

I lie there and listen to the sound of slippers on the kitchen floor.

I tap my good luck song against the wall over and over, but I hear the rain and know I will not go to the park today.

Tomorrow it will be a nice day. Tomorrow my sister will feel better, and I will go to the park and find Abram. He will make my balloon as good as new.

Now I walk over to the window and lean my head against it. The rain taps its song to me against the glass, and I tap back.

Think about the story. Finish the chart on page 383.
Then answer the questions.

1. Use your chart. How does the boy learn what the
   weather is each day?

2. Use your chart. How does the boy describe his
   sister? How does he feel about her? Tell why you
   think as you do.

3. Look at the pictures in the story. Why aren't they
   clear? How do the pictures help you understand
   how the boy feels?

4. Think about what Abram says when he gives the
   boy the balloon. Whom might the balloon stand for?
   Tell why you think as you do.

5. The boy cannot see colors, but he learns about
   them. What does he learn about colors from
   Abram?

6. What do you think happens to the boy on the day
   after the story ends?

7. The selections in this unit are about how people
   see things differently from one another. How do
   Abram and the boy's sister see the trees in the
   park differently?

The boy's sister says that the park is ugly and dirty. Abram says that you can see what you want to see. Talk about how different people see things. Which person do you think is right, and why? Ask questions about what your classmates say.

Focusing on "frog," "Some People," "Metaphor," and "Dreams"

▶ Think about a time you had difficulty describing something to another person. Talk about how you solved your problem. Ask questions about what your classmates say.

▶ Read the titles of the poems on pages 402–405. Look at the pictures. Think about what you know about describing something.
- What might each poem be describing?
- What way of describing things might each writer use?

▶ Get ready to read these four poems. As you read, think about the things the writer is comparing. Think about what you would add to this chart.

Poem	Thing Being Compared	What It Is Compared To

Now turn the page and read the poems. Then you will talk about poems that use metaphors or similes.

frog

A poem by Valerie Worth

The spotted frog
Sits quite still
On a wet stone;

He is green
With a luster
Of water on his skin;

His back is mossy
With spots, and green
Like moss on a stone;

His gold-circled eyes
Stare hard
Like bright metal rings;

When he leaps
He is like a stone
Thrown into the pond;

Water rings spread
After him, bright circles
Of green, circles of gold.

402

Illustrated by Christa Kieffer

Some People

A poem by Rachel Field

Isn't it strange some people make
    You feel so tired inside,
Your thoughts begin to shrivel up
    Like leaves all brown and dried!

But when you're with some other one
    It's stranger still to find
Your thoughts as thick as fireflies
    All shiny in your mind!

Illustrated by Francis Livingston

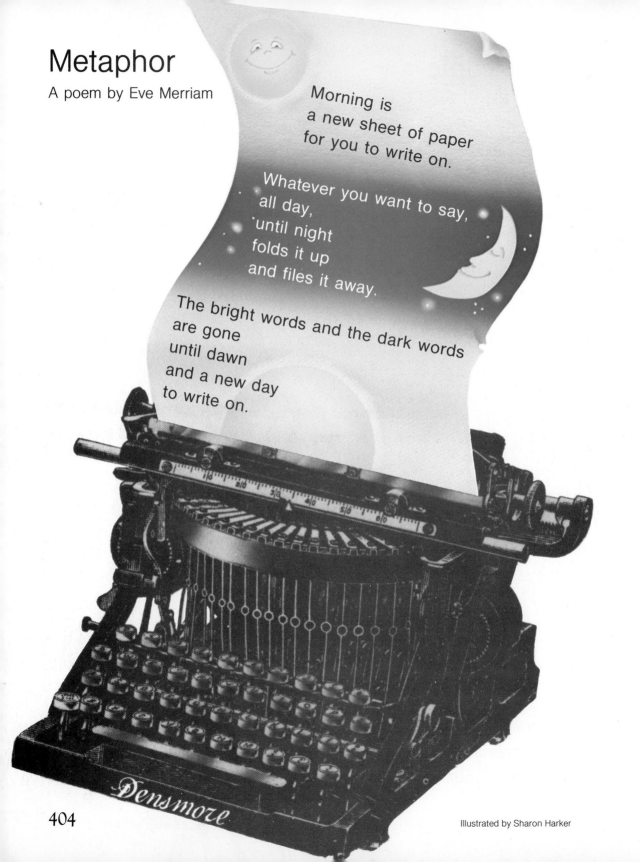

Metaphor

A poem by Eve Merriam

Morning is
a new sheet of paper
for you to write on.

Whatever you want to say,
all day,
until night
folds it up
and files it away.

The bright words and the dark words
are gone
until dawn
and a new day
to write on.

Illustrated by Sharon Harker

Dreams

A poem by Langston Hughes

Hold fast to dreams
For if dreams die
Life is a broken-winged bird
That cannot fly.

Hold fast to dreams
For when dreams go
Life is a barren field
Frozen with snow.

Illustrated by Francis Livingston

Langston Hughes, one of America's great poets, came to national attention almost by accident. He was working as a busboy in a hotel restaurant in Washington, DC. One night he saw Vachel Lindsay, a famous poet, eating in the restaurant. Too shy to speak, Langston Hughes instead dropped three of his poems at Vachel Lindsay's plate. That evening Mr. Lindsay praised these poems and read them to a large group of people. The next morning newspaper reporters interviewed Langston Hughes and took his picture in his busboy's uniform. His poems appeared in the newspaper. Soon he was publishing his works in books and newspapers.

In addition to poetry, Langston Hughes wrote stories, plays, books, and operas. Much of his writing is about his experiences as a member of the black community. His writing has helped others to understand and appreciate this experience.

Books of Poetry by Langston Hughes

The Dream Keeper

Selected Poems of Langston Hughes

Think about the poems. Finish the chart on page 401. Then answer the questions.

1. Use your chart. Think about "frog." What different things about the subject does the writer describe? To what are the things compared?

2. Use your chart. Think about "Dreams." What two things does the writer use to stand for life?

3. Imagine that a third verse of "Dreams" begins:
   > Hold fast to dreams
   > For if dreams stay

   What might the writer use to stand for life?

4. Use your chart. Think about "Some People." What two things stand for thoughts? Tell what kinds of people cause these thoughts.

5. Use your chart. Think about "Metaphor." What does the sheet of paper stand for? Why does the writer choose that symbol?

6. Think of another symbol the writer of "Metaphor" might have used for a new day.

Why do poets and writers use similes and metaphors? Why don't they just say what they mean? Talk about what similes and metaphors add to a person's writing. Ask questions about what your classmates say.

WORK IN A GROUP

Learn About POETRY

Similes and Metaphors by Myra Cohn Livingston

Poets have exciting ways to help us see things differently and more clearly. For example, when one thing reminds them of another, poets may describe how these two things are alike by comparing them. These imaginative comparisons are called *similes* (SIM•uh•lees) and *metaphors* (MET•uh•fawrz). Poets use them to help us see something in a new way.

A simile is usually introduced by the words *like* or *as.* In her poem "frog," Valerie Worth uses three similes.

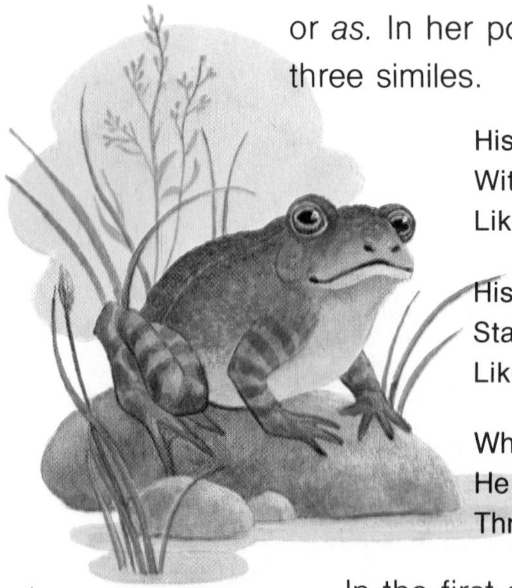

His back is mossy
With spots, and green
Like moss on a stone;

His gold-circled eyes
Stare hard
Like bright metal rings;

When he leaps
He is like a stone
Thrown into the pond;

In the first simile, the poet compares the green of the frog's back to moss on a stone and says that

the moss and the frog's back are similar. In the next simile, the frog's eyes remind the poet of bright, metal rings. When the frog leaps, the poet says he is like a stone thrown into the pond.

Similes can be created about everything we know. In her poem "Some People," Rachel Field has two similes about thoughts.

> Your thoughts begin to shrivel up
> Like leaves all brown and dried!

Have your thoughts ever seemed like dried-up leaves? Perhaps, at times, they are

> . . . as thick as fireflies
> All shiny in your mind!

Poets also use metaphors to compare two different things. A poet usually introduces a metaphor with the word *is*. In his poem "Dreams," Langston Hughes uses metaphor to give us a vivid picture of what would happen if dreams should die. He says more than "life would be bad" or "things would be terrible." Instead, he paints a picture for us to see.

Life is a broken-winged bird
That cannot fly.

. . . .

Life is a barren field
Frozen with snow.

By using a metaphor, Langston Hughes gives us a new way of looking at life. So does poet Eve Merriam, who tells us how she feels about the day in her poem "Metaphor." How does the poet give us a new way of looking at the day in these first three lines from her poem?

Morning is
a new sheet of paper
for you to write on.

Now look at some things around you. Look at the shapes of clouds, people you know, buildings, windows, trees, rocks—even your own thoughts and dreams—and make your own similes and metaphors. You'll discover an exciting way of looking at and thinking about the world!

TALKING ABOUT THE SELECTIONS

You have read these selections.

Mexicali Soup
The Turkey or the Eagle?
The Monkey and the Crocodile
Sound of Sunshine, Sound of Rain
frog
Some People
Metaphor
Dreams

Talk about the selections you have read. Consider how the ideas and characters are alike and different. Talk about the theme.

1. What characters in the stories does the poem "Some People" remind you of? Why?

2. Do you think the sister in "Sound of Sunshine, Sound of Rain" would fit into Mama's family in "Mexicali Soup"? Tell why you think as you do.

3. Which character in the selections most needs to change? Tell why you think as you do.

4. Which character learns the most when two paths cross? What does he or she learn?

BOOKSHELF

The Not-just-anybody Family by Betsy Byars. Delacorte, 1986. Junior tries out his wings and everyone else has zany mishaps. This happens on what is just an ordinary day for the unforgettable Blossom family.

Hello, My Name Is Scrambled Eggs by Jamie Gilson. Lothrop, Lee & Shepard, 1985. A Vietnamese refugee family comes to stay in Harvey's house. Harvey decides to give the son an American education and gets an education himself.

The Great Bamboozlement by Jane Flory. Houghton Mifflin, 1982. In pioneer days a family trades their Pennsylvania farm for a floating store and sets off down the Monongahela River only to find themselves in the middle of trouble.

Do You Have the Time, Lydia? by Evaline Ness. E. P. Dutton, 1971. Lydia starts many projects, but she never finishes what she begins. When her brother asks her to build a box car with him, Lydia never seems to have the time to help.

Three Wishes by Lucille Clifton. Viking, 1976. When Zenobia finds a penny with her birth year on it, her friend Victor tells her she will be granted three wishes.

LITERARY TERMS

CHARACTER(S) *The people (or animals) in a story, poem, or play.* Sometimes authors are concerned mainly with bringing their story characters to life. How the characters think, feel, act, and change is more important than the story's main action, or *plot.* For example, in "Spunky Ramona," author Beverly Cleary gives us much information about Ramona Quimby. We learn what Ramona thinks and feels and how she acts. The story is *about Ramona,* not just about the events in Ramona's life. Other stories, such as "The Case of the Missing Roller Skates," are built mainly around the plot.

CHARACTERIZATION *The ways in which writers present and develop characters to make the characters seem real.* Here are several ways in which writers develop their characters:

1. *By describing how the character looks* **"Her delicate face glowed like a peach beginning to ripen in the summer sun. And her dark eyes sparkled in the dancing firelight."**

2. *By showing the character's words and actions* **"Pa did not whistle about his work as usual, and after a while he said, 'And what we'll do in a wild country without a good watchdog I don't know.'"**

3. *By telling the character's thoughts and feelings* **"I do not want anyone to sit with me, but he is sitting with me now. I am afraid I will spill and he will see me."**

4. *By telling what others think of the character* **"Mama was a wonderful cook."**

5. *By stating something about the character* **"After all, Wilbur was a very young pig—not much more than a baby, really."**

DIALOGUE   *Conversation between or among characters.* Dialogue is used in almost all forms of literature to move the *plot,* or main action, forward and to tell the reader something about the characters. In the story "The Case of the Missing Roller Skates," author Donald J. Sobol uses dialogue to show how Encyclopedia Brown solved the case:

> **"We just want to be sure you weren't in Dr. Vivian Wilson's office this morning. That's all," said Sally.**
> **"Well, I wasn't. I had a sprained wrist, not a toothache. So why should I go near his office?" demanded Billy.**

These few lines of dialogue give the reader enough information to guess the solution of the case.

Dialogue is especially important in plays, where conversation is the main way to tell the story and to show each character's personality. In the play *Paddington Goes to the Hospital,* Paddington and a doctor named Sir Archibald discuss Mr. Curry, a patient at the hospital:

> **Sir Archibald: Are you a friend of his?**
> **Paddington: Well, I'm not really a friend. He lives next door and I've brought him some food.**
> **Sir Archibald: Food! That's the last thing he needs. It will only make him stay longer. That man's entirely without scruples.**

Through his conversation, the reader learns that Sir Archibald is upset because he feels that

Mr. Curry is taking advantage of the hospital.

See also **Play.**

FABLE *A brief story that teaches a lesson.* Many fables state the lesson, or *moral,* at the end of the story. The characters in fables are often animals that speak and act like people. The best-known fables were written long ago in Greece by a man named Aesop. "The Lion and the Mouse" is one of Aesop's fables.

FANTASY *A fiction story with fanciful characters and plots.* A fantasy may take place in a world much like one you know. Yet in the "real world" presented in a fantasy story, ordinary people and animals do impossible things. In the fantasy story *Charlotte's Web,* for example, an ordinary farm contains a pig that can talk and a spider that can write.

Often, however, fantasies take place in imaginary kingdoms or worlds that are quite different from the real world. Writer C. S. Lewis has created the fantasy Kingdom of Narnia in his series of seven books called *The Chronicles of Narnia*. It is a world filled with unusual creatures and magical events.

The different kinds of fantasy offer us the chance to wonder *"What if...?" What if* you could be three inches tall, or ride a magic carpet, or travel through time?

See also **Fiction.**

FICTION *A story invented by the writer*. A work of fiction may be *based* on real events, but it always includes made-up (fictional) characters and experiences. A work of fiction may be brief, like a fable, a folk tale, or a short story, or it may be a book-length story called a **novel.**

FOLK TALE *A fiction story made up long ago and handed down in written or spoken form*. Many folk tales have no known authors. Though folk tales come from different parts of the world, many characters, plots, and ideas in them are similar. *Fairy tales,* like the story "Cinderella," are a kind of folk tale.

METAPHOR   *A way of comparing how two different things are alike.* A metaphor *suggests* a comparison by saying that one thing *is* another: "This car **is** a lemon" or "The sun **was** a bright, new penny." Writers use metaphors to help us picture things in new ways.

See also **Simile.**

NONFICTION   *A true (factual) story; any writing that describes things as they actually happened, or that presents information or opinions about something.* One type of nonfiction is the written history of a person's life. When a person writes his or her own life story, it is an **autobiography.** When someone else writes a person's life story, it is a **biography.** Other common forms of nonfiction include news reports, travel stories, personal journals and diaries, and articles on science or history.

PLAY   *A story that is acted out, usually on a stage, by actors.* In its written form, a play begins with a **cast of characters,** or a list of the people, or sometimes animals, in the play. A play has a *plot,* or action, just like a story. However, a play is meant to be acted out. The characters in a play tell the story through their words, or **dialogue.**

During a play the actors follow **stage directions,** which tell them *how* to act and speak. Stage directions may also describe the **setting,** where the action takes place. Stage directions are usually not read aloud when a play is acted out.

See also **Dialogue.**

PLOT   *The action in a story.* When you tell what happens in a story, you are talking about the plot. For instance, in the story "The Escape," by E. B. White, the plot tells how Wilbur, a young pig, escapes from his pen to see the world but is lured back with a bucket of slops.

The plot is also the writer's overall *plan* of the action—how, when, and why things happen. The writer uses this plan to arrange the action in an interesting and reasonable order. Each happening becomes a link in a chain of events that makes sense and holds the reader's attention.

The most important part of a plot is **conflict,** a character's struggle with opposing forces. Sometimes a character struggles with nature (as in the story "An Eskimo Birthday"). Sometimes a character struggles with another character (as in Eleanor Estes's "The Ghost in the Attic"). At other times the conflict is within the character's own mind. In the story "The Escape" by E. B. White, for example, Wilbur the pig struggles to decide whether

he should give up his freedom in return for food.

SETTING *When and where a story takes place.* If you say, "Today at school Susan won a race," you have given the setting (when and where) before describing the action. Writers can choose any time or place as a setting for a story. In the story "The Black Fox," writer Betsy Byars gives us a clear picture of how the ravine looked to Tom.

This was my favorite place in the forest. The sides of the ravine were heavy dark boulders with mosses and ferns growing between the rocks, and at the bottom were trunks of old dead trees. The tree trunks were like statues in some old jungle temple, idols that had fallen and broken and would soon be lost in the creeping foliage. There was only an occasional patch of sunlight.

The writer does not always give us the setting so directly. Sometimes we figure it out as the story goes along. Most stories include several different types of information about where and when the story takes place. For instance, at the beginning of the story "An Eskimo Birthday," by Tom D. Robinson, the action begins in a schoolroom during a snowstorm. As the story continues, we find out that the school is part of a modern Eskimo village in Alaska.

SIMILE *A way of comparing how two different things are alike.* Writers use similes to surprise us or to make us look at our world in a new way. Similes are different from metaphors because they use the words *like* or *as*. In the story "Sound of Sunshine, Sound of Rain," writer Florence Parry Heide describes a voice using a simile to compare two things: "My sister's voice is little and sharp and high **like** needles flying in the air."

See also **Metaphor.**

GLOSSARY

This glossary gives the meanings of unfamiliar words used in the text of this book. The meanings given here define words only the way they are used in the book. You can find other meanings for these words in the dictionary.

The correct pronunciation of each glossary word is given in the special spelling after that word. The sounds used in these spellings are explained in the following Pronunciation Key. Each symbol, or letter, stands for a sound, a sound you can recognize in the words following it. In addition to these sounds, each glossary pronunciation includes marks to show the kind of force, or stress, with which certain syllables are pronounced. A heavy mark, ′, shows that the syllable it follows is given the strongest, or primary stress, as in **re·fined** (re·fīnd′). A lighter mark, ′, shows that the syllable it follows is given a secondary, or lighter, stress, as in **sou·ve·nir** (sōō′·və·nir′).

Several abbreviations are used in the glossary: *v.,* verb; *n.,* noun; *adj.,* adjective; *adv.,* adverb; *pl.,* plural.

Pronunciation Key

a	add, map	m	move, seem	u	up, done
ā	ace, rate	n	nice, tin	û(r)	urn, term
â(r)	care, air	ng	ring, song	yōō	use, few
ä	palm, father	o	odd, hot	v	vain, eve
b	bat, rub	ō	open, so	w	win, away
ch	check, catch	ô	order, jaw	y	yet, yearn
d	dog, rod	oi	oil, boy	z	zest, muse
e	end, pet	ou	out, now	zh	vision, pleasure
ē	even, tree	ōō	pool, food	ə	the schwa,
f	fit, half	o͝o	took, full		an unstressed
g	go, log	p	pit, stop		vowel representing
h	hope, hate	r	run, poor		the sound spelled
i	it, give	s	see, pass		a in above
ī	ice, write	sh	sure, rush		e in sicken
j	joy, ledge	t	talk, sit		i in possible
k	cool, take	th	thin, both		o in melon
l	look, rule	t͟h	this, bathe		u in circus

A

ac·cu·mu·lat·ing (ə·kyōō′·myōō·lāt′·ing) *adj.* Piling up; collecting.

a·dapt (ə·dapt′) *v.* To change.

al·fal·fa (al·fal′·fə) *n.* A cloverlike plant used for cattle feed.

al·ler·gy (al′·ûr·jē) *n.* A sensitivity that causes symptoms of illness.

ant·lers (ant′·lûrz) *n.* Horns of members of the deer family.

anx·ious (ang′·shəs) *adj.* Worried, uneasy.

ap·pe·tiz·ing (ap′·ə·tī′·zing) *adj.* Appealing in appearance or smell.

arc (ärk) *n.* Something that forms an arch or a curve.

a·rith·me·tic (ə·rith′·mə·tik) *n.* Calculation using numbers.

ar·mor (är′·mûr) *n.* Defensive covering.

ar·ro·gance (âr′·ə·gəns) *n.* Too much pride and too little regard for others.

as·sault (ə·sôlt′) *n.* A violent attack.

a·strad·dle (ə·strad′·əl) *adv.* With one leg on each side.

awe·some (ô′·səm) *adj.* Inspiring feelings of wonder and fear.

B

bab·ble (bab′·əl) *v.* To make meaningless sounds.

ba·leen (bə·lēn′) *n.* The easily bent material that hangs from the upper jaw of whales and that strains the tiny sea animals on which they feed.

barge (bärj) *n.* A flat-bottomed boat used for carrying cargo.

bar·ren (bar′·ən) *adj.* Without growth; empty; lacking crops or trees or other plants.

bed·lam (bed′·ləm) *n.* A place or condition of noise or confusion.

bes·ti·ar·y (bes′·chē·er′·ē) *n.* A book of fables about the habits of actual and mythical animals.

blanched (blancht) *v.* Turned pale.

blunt (blunt) *adj.* Having a tip or point that is not sharp.

blus·ter·ing (blus′·tər·ing) *adj.* Speaking in a noisy, boastful, or bullying manner.

bolt (bōlt) *n.* A roll of cloth.

boun·da·ry (boun′·də·rē) *n.* A border.

brand·ing (brand′·ing) *v.* Marking with a hot tool.

bub·bler (bub′·lûr) *n.* A water fountain.

C

ca·nal (kə·nal′) *n.* A waterway dug across land, connecting already existing bodies of water.

cap·tiv·i·ty (kap·tiv′·ə·tē) *n.* The state of being held prisoner.

ca·reen·ing (kə·rēn′·ing) *adj.* Lurching; moving rapidly in an uncontrolled way.

ca·reer (kə·rir′) *n.* Work one chooses and trains for.

car·i·bou (kar′·ə·bōō) *n.* A large North American deer closely related to reindeer.

cat·tle (kat′·əl) *n.* A word for cows.

cham·ber (chām′·bər) *n.* A cave or an enclosed space.

col·lapse (kə·laps′) *v.* To cave or fall in completely.

col·league (kol′·ēg) *n.* A member of the same profession.

Co·man·che (kə·man′·chē) *n.* A group of American Indians living in Wyoming and Nebraska and south into New Mexico and northwestern Texas.

com·mo·tion (kə·mō′·shən) *n.* Noisy confusion or disturbance.

con·sci·en·tious (kon′·shē·en′·shəs) *adj.* Being careful to do things correctly and to be good.

con·tra·dict (kon′·trə·dikt′) *v.* To deny (a statement).

con·ven·tion (kən·ven′·chən) *n.* A group of people meeting for a single purpose, such as to organize a government or to select candidates for office.

cor·ri·dor (kôr′·ə·dər) *n.* A hallway.

cun·ning (kun′·ing) *n.* Slyness or cleverness in getting something.

cur·sive (kûr′·siv) *n.* Handwriting in which the strokes of the letters are joined in each word.

D

daze (dāz) *v.* To confuse.

de·clared (dē·clârd′) *v.* Announced formally.

de·fi·ant (di·fī′·ənt) *adj.* Boldly refusing to obey.

de·hy·dra·tion (dē·hī·drā′·shun) *n.* Loss of water.

de·mol·ished (di·mol′·isht) *adj.* Torn down completely; ruined.

di·ag·no·sis (dī′·əg·nō′·səs) *n.* A conclusion reached as to the nature of an illness or disease, based on an examination.

dig (dig) *n.* An archaeological excavation or its site.

dig·ni·fied (dig′·nə·fīd) *adj.* Honorable, stately.

dis·in·te·grate (dis·in′·tə·grāt′) *v.* To break down into small parts.

dis·loy·al (dis·loi′·əl) *adj.* Breaking faith; not supporting another.

dis·solve (di·zolv′) *v.* To disappear.

do·sage (dō′·sij) *n.* The amount of medicine that must be taken.

dron·ing (drōn′·ing) *v.* Making a continuous humming or buzzing sound with little variation.

drought (drout) *n.* A long period of time without rain.

E

ec·cen·tric (ek·sen′·trik) *adj.* Strange, odd.

ef·fort·less·ly (ef′·ərt·ləs·lē) *adv.* Requiring little physical power.

el·e·gant (el′·i·gənt) *adj.* Luxurious and beautiful.

e·merge (i·mûrj′) *v.* To come up into view.

em·ploy·ees (im·ploi′·ēz) *n.* People hired by another.

en·vi·ron·ments (en·vī′·rən·mənts) *n.* Surroundings.

F

fam·ine (fam′·in) *n.* A great shortage of food.

fan·ta·sy (fan′·tə·sē) *n.* A fiction story with fanciful characters and plots.

fash·ion (fash′·ən) *v.* To carve, mold, or give shape to.

fast (fast) *adv.* Tightly.

fear·some (fir′·səm) *adj.* Scary.

fine (fīn) *adj.* Clear; sunny; used in speaking about the weather.

flint (flint) *n.* A hard stone that is easy to shape into sharp tools and arrowheads.

flush (flush) *v.* To drive or frighten (game birds) from cover.

folk·lore (fōk′·lôr′) *n.* The stories, traditions, and superstitions of a group of people.

folk·lor·ist (fōk′·lôr′·əst) *n.* A person who studies the traditional beliefs, stories, and customs of a people or culture.

frank·in·cense (frangk′·in·sens) *n.* A gum or resin from various Arabian and African trees, often burned as incense for its sweet, spicy smell.

fren·zy (fren′·zē) *n.* A fit of wild or violent acitivity.

G

gap·ing (gāp′·ing) *adj.* Wide open.

gasp (gasp) *v.* To draw in one's breath quickly in surprise.

glow·er (glou'·ər) v. To glare; to look or stare at angrily.

gnaw (nô) v. To chew.

grope (grōp) v. To feel about in the dark in search; to look for something in the dark.

H

harsh (härsh) adj. Fierce.

hearth (härth) n. The fireside.

hinged (hinjd) n. Jointed.

hys·ter·ics (his·ter'·iks) n., pl. Sudden uncontrolled laughter.

I

im·mi·grant (im'·i·grənt) n. A person who has left a native country to live in another country.

im·pact (im'·pakt) n. A striking of one body against another.

in·dus·try (in'·dus·trē) n. A business.

in·vest (in·vest') v. To spend money in order to earn more.

J

jeer·ing (jir'·ing) adj. Insulting; teasing in a mean way.

K

keg (keg) n. A small barrel.

ki·mo·no (kə·mō'·nə) n. A loose robe with short, wide sleeves and a sash, traditional to Japan.

L

lar·der (lar'·dûr) n. A pantry or place where food is kept.

lead (lēd) n. A clue.

lure (loor) v. To tempt or entice, especially into danger.

lus·ter (lus'·tər) n. Brightness.

M

maid·en (mād'·ən) n. A young unmarried woman.

mal·let (mal'·ət) n. A hammer with a large head.

ma·nure (mə·noor') n. Waste material from barns and barnyards used to improve the soil.

mid·dlings (mid'·lings) n. A mixture of coarsely ground wheat and bran used for animal feed.

mi·rac·u·lous (mə·rak'·yə·ləs) adj. Marvelous; similar to a miracle.

mis·er·a·ble (miz'·ər·ə·bəl) adj. Very unhappy.

mourn·ers (môr′·nərz) *n.* People who express sorrow for someone who is dead.

mourn·ing (môr′·ning) *adj.* Making a low, continuous sound that seems to express sorrow or grief.

muk·luk (mək′·lək′) *n.* A soft Eskimo boot made of sealskin or reindeer skin.

myrrh (mûr) *n.* A fragrant gum resin from any of several plants of Arabia and Africa used in making incense and perfume.

N
---

nav·i·gate (nav′·ə·gāt′) *v.* To steer or guide a boat or ship.

nudge (nuj) *v.* To get someone's attention by a push of the elbow.

O
---

om·i·nous (om′·ə·nəs) *adj.* Threatening; being an evil omen.

or·ga·nized (ôr′·gə·nīzd) *v.* Formed as a whole, or placed in an order.

out·crop·ping (out′·krop′·ing) *n.* The coming out, at or above the ground, of a mineral.

out·skirts (out′·skûrtz′) *n., pl.* The edges of a city.

P
---

pan·try (pan′·trē) *n.* A small room off the kitchen, where food or kitchen supplies are stored.

par·ka (pär′·kə) *n.* A fur or cloth jacket or coat with a hood.

peas·ant (pez′·ənt) *n.* A poor farmer.

peer (pir) *n.* A person of one's own age group.

per·sist (pər·sist′) *v.* To go on stubbornly even though opposed.

pet·ro·le·um (pet·rō′·lē·um) *n.* Oil.

pit·i·ful (pit′·i·fəl) *adj.* Worthy of pity or sympathy.

plume (plo̅o̅m) *n.* A large showy feather.

pot (pot) *n.* Jar.

pro·ces·sion (prə·sesh′·ən) *n.* A long line of people moving in a slow, orderly manner.

punc·tu·al (pungk′·cho̅o·wəl) *adj.* Being on time; prompt.

Q
---

queer (que̅r) *adj.* Strange, odd.

R

range (rānj) *n.* Open land where cattle can roam.

ra·vine (rə·vēn') *n.* A long, deep hollow in the earth, usually formed by the action of a stream.

re·ac·tion (rē·ak'·shən) *n.* The act of answering quickly with little thought.

re·cess (rē'·ses) *n.* A hidden or secret place.

re·fined (re·fīnd') *adj.* Free from anything coarse.

re·in·force·ment (rē'·in·fôrs'·mənt) *n.* A new member sent to help troops already in action.

re·lapse (rē'·laps) *n.* A falling back into an illness after improving.

re·luc·tant·ly (ri·luk'·tənt·lē) *adv.* Unwillingly; holding back.

re·proach (ri·prōch') *n.* Blame.

re·sem·ble (ri·zem'·bəl) *v.* To look like or be similar to.

res·o·lu·tion (rez'·ə·lōō'·shən) *n.* A promise to oneself.

re·spec·ta·ble (rē·spek'·tə·bəl) *adj.* Deserving respect.

roam (rōm) *v.* To travel without purpose or plan; to wander.

rough·neck (ruf'·nek') *n.* A rough, rude, or disorderly person.

ruff (ruf) *n.* A high, full collar; in this case, made of fur.

runt (rənt) *n.* The smallest animal in a litter.

S

sac·ri·fice (sak'·rə·fīs) *v.* To make an offering of something precious.

sal·a·ry (sal'·ə·rē) *n.* Money paid for services.

scorn (skôrn) *n.* A feeling of disgust.

scrunch (skrunch) *v.* To squeeze together into a small bundle.

scru·ple (skrōō'·pəl) *n.* A misgiving or objection about something that one thinks is wrong.

sha·man (shā'·mən) *n.* An important member of an American Indian tribe.

shriv·el up (shriv'·əl up) *v.* To wrinkle and dry up.

shrugged (shrugd) *v.* Drew up the shoulders to show that one didn't care.

shut·tle (shut'·əl) *n.* A device used in weaving to carry a thread from side to side between the threads that run lengthwise.

sieve (siv) *n.* A utensil made of wire mesh or metal with many small holes, used for straining.

slops (slops) *n., pl.* Leftover food fed to animals.

snare (snâr) *n.* A kind of trap used to catch small animals, usually with a noose that jerks tight.

snow ma·chine (snō mə·shēn′) *n.* A machine that travels over snow; also called a *snowmobile.*

sod (sod) *n.* Ground covered with grass.

sol·i·tude (sol′·ə·tōōd′) *n.* The condition of being alone.

sooth·ing (sōōth′·ing) *adj.* Calming.

sou·ve·nir (sōō′·və·nir′) *n.* Something that is kept as a reminder of a place, a person, or an occasion.

span·iel (span′·yul) *n.* A medium-sized, long-haired breed of dog.

spec·ta·cles (spek′·tə·kəlz) *n., pl.* A pair of eyeglasses.

spunk·y (spungk′·ē) *adj.* Courageous; spirited.

sub·side (səb·sīd′) *v.* To become less or quiet.

suf·fo·cat·ing (suf′·ə·kāt′·ing) *adj.* Making uncomfortable by not allowing one to breathe.

su·i·cide (sōō′·ə·sīd′) *n.* The act of losing one's life by one's own choice.

sur·geon (sûr′·jən) *n.* A doctor who can operate on people.

sus·pect (sus′·pekt) *n.* A person who is thought to be guilty of a wrongdoing.

swap·ping (swop′·ing) *v.* Trading or exchanging.

T

thatched (thacht) *adj.* Covered with straw, especially on the roof of a house.

thrash·ing (thrash′·ing) *v.* Swinging, rolling, or moving around wildly and rapidly.

thrum (thrum) *n.* The ends of thread left on a loom after the cloth has been cut off. *v.* To pluck on, as a guitar; to strum.

toi·let wa·ter (toi′·lət wô′·tər) *n.* A light-scented liquid, like perfume.

troll (trōl) *n.* In folk tales, a troublesome creature, either dwarf or giant, who lives in caves, in hills, or under bridges.

trough (trof) *n.* A long, narrow, open food or water container for an animal.

trudge (truj) *v.* To walk wearily or with great effort.

V

---

valve (valv) *n.* A mechanical device that opens and shuts to start or stop the flow of a liquid or gas.

vault·like (vôlt′·līk′) *adj.* Built with arches or curves.

W

---

weft (weft) *n.* In weaving, the threads carried by the shuttle from side to side across the fixed threads in a loom; also known as the *woof.*

whim·per (hwim′·pûr) *v.* Whine.

whisked (hwiskd) *v.* Moved quickly and lightly.

wol·ver·ine (wŏŏl′·və·rēn′) *n.* A meat-eating animal of the weasel family, having blackish, shaggy hair with white markings.

0
1
2
G 3
H 4
I 5
J 6